6

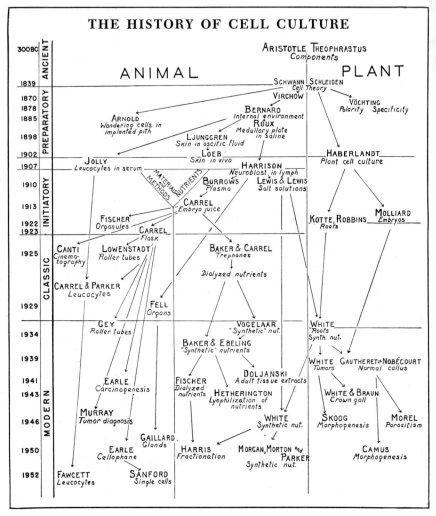

FIGURE 1. This chart shows some of the major events in the development of the field of cell culture. Names and events have been chosen because they appear to have some noteworthy place in the story, either because they constitute significant steps along the way, as in the case of Carrel's introduction of the use of embryo extract which opened up whole fields of activity; or because they foreshadowed some later significant event, as was the case with Ljunggren's cultures of skin.

It is divided horizontally into chronological periods, vertically into fields of activity, and where possible I have indicated what appear to be the lines of dependence of ideas. My own lines have crossed the boundary between animal and plant cell culture twice, once at the beginning, because I owe so much of my point of view and approach to the work of Warren and Margaret Lewis that my studies on plant tissue nutrition derive quite directly from their work on animal cell nutrition; and a second time when I took the methods I had elaborated with plant tissues and stepped back to try to apply them to the problems of animal cell culture. In the same way Harrison (1928) acknowledged his indebtedness to Haberlandt (1902) across the same boundary.

THE CULTIVATION OF
ANIMAL AND PLANT CELLS

By

PHILIP R. WHITE

Research Associate
Roscoe B. Jackson Memorial Laboratory
Bar Harbor, Maine

THE RONALD PRESS COMPANY ⟋ NEW YORK

2

Library of Congress Catalog Card Number: 54–6980

PRINTED IN THE UNITED STATES OF AMERICA

DEDICATION

To ALL THOSE RESTLESS SPIRITS who, wandering beyond the narrow boundaries of established pastures, keep the paths between fields open and in the process occasionally find here and there a tussock which is in truth greener, more nourishing and worthy to be used for the seeding of new fields, I dedicate this volume.

"Entia non sunt multiplicanda praeter
necessitatem"
"Things are not to be made more complicated
than necessary."

—WILLIAM OF OCCAM, 1270–1349

FOREWORD

THREE OBJECTIVES have been sought in the preparation of this book: To present all the major techniques of cell culture for both plant and animal materials in a sufficiently extended and detailed fashion so that they can be used by all those who may choose to enter the field professionally; to present a group of simple techniques by which anyone without previous experience beyond that of a good biology course may be able to make interesting and effective, if less professional, cultures and may perhaps be led gradually into the greater refinements of the field; and to emphasize as adequately as is conveniently possible the essential importance of the cell itself, as the basic physiological entity out of which all those societies called "organisms" (or at least almost all of them) are constituted.

This is *not* a book on "tissue culture." It deals with the cultivation of cells. The term "tissue culture" has always been a misnomer, as Harrison pointed out long ago (1928). One does not cultivate "tissues." What one does is to cultivate either a group of cells such as those which make up certain "tissues," or an organ, itself made up of "tissues" but never a tissue itself. This has long bothered thoughtful cell culturists. Yet most investigators have avoided the term "cell culture," probably because to some it has seemed to mean the cultivation of "single-celled animals." This too is incorrect. There are no such things as "single-celled animals." A "cell" basically means a structural division of an

v

organism. An organism does not possess "cells" unless it can be divided into these units. If it cannot be so divided it is not "unicellular" but "noncellular." The bacteria, protozoa, and syncytial protophyta are noncellular, not unicellular. Steward and Martin (1937) raised this objection with reference to the misuse of the term "cell" for a *Valonia* coenocyte. When I exclude the bacteria, molds, coenocytic algae, protozoa and even such complex organisms as the Radiolaria, from cell culture and relegate them rather to the distinct field of microbiology, I am merely going back to original meanings. And in so doing I am emphasizing a fact to which I will return again and again in the text itself, the fact that in all this "tissue culture" or "cell culture" work, what we are really seeking to do is to treat the *cell* as a definite physiological unit.

I have sought to strip from the study of this subject its former atmosphere of mystery and complication. The gray walls, black gowns, masks and hoods; the shining, twisted glass and pulsating colored fluids; the gleaming stainless steel, hidden steam jets, enclosed microscopes and huge witches' caldrons of the "great" laboratories of "tissue culture" have led far too many persons to consider cell culture too abstruse, recondite, and sacrosanct a field to be invaded by mere *hoi polloi!* Science stifles in too rare an atmosphere. Thirty years of experience with plant materials and ten with animal cells convince me that anyone with average manual ability and the equipment available in the usual high-school biology laboratory *can* make cell cultures—successful ones. They may not be elaborate, nor will they survive for long periods. But every biology student should at some time have the dramatic experience of seeing the rhythmic beat of heart muscle, the sweep of the cilia of pulmonary epithelium, the twitching of skeletal muscle, the peristalsis of chorioallantoic or intestinal vesicles, the migration of fibroblasts, and the spread of nerve fibres. And every student can not only see these things but have the thrill of preparing them himself. The cell culture technique should be a part of every biological laboratory's program instead of being hidden in a few great institutions.

I have tried to keep the presentation as simple and concise as seems compatible with completeness and lucidity, and have wherever possible used photographs and drawings in place of long descriptions. I have not attempted an inclusive survey of the field in all its past and present ramifications. In fact, I have sedulously avoided such a survey, which seems to me to be of interest chiefly to the specialist, for whom, after all, this book is not intended. I have concentrated rather on those matters which may suggest to the student new fields of conquest and provide him with the basic information and the techniques necessary for an intelligent approach to those fields.

PHILIP R. WHITE

Bar Harbor, Maine
March, 1954

ACKNOWLEDGMENTS

ONE DOES NOT prepare a book alone. I should like especially to acknowledge the help of Dr. Donald M. Pace of the University of Nebraska, Dr. Ralph Wetmore of Harvard, Dr. Betty Danes of the University of Iowa School of Medicine, Dr. Charity Waymouth of the Chester Beatty Research Institute, Royal Cancer Hospital, London, and Dr. William F. Millington of this Laboratory, all of whom have read and criticized preliminary drafts of the manuscript and have made helpful criticisms and suggestions. I should also like to express my gratitude to Drs. Albert Fischer, Honor B. Fell, Margaret R. Murray, George O. Gey and Wilton R. Earle for their portraits, which are new in this volume, and to Prof. Roger J. Gautheret for a more up-to-date picture than that I had previously used. Dr. Fell's portrait is published with the permission of Messrs. J. Russell & Sons, London, to whom I wish to express my thanks. Photographs for my use have been supplied by The Rockefeller Institute for Medical Research, The Carnegie Laboratories of Embryology and the Boyce Thompson Institute, Wm. Boekel & Co., Inc., Dr. Theodore S. Hauschka, Arthur H. Thomas & Co., Dr. Don Fawcett, Dr. Folke Skoog, Dr. Morgan Harris, Dr. Peter J. Gaillard, Dr. Honor B. Fell, Dr. Georges Morel, and Dr. Charles M. Pomerat. I should like to thank them for permission to publish or republish these pictures. The Selas Corporation of America has graciously prepared one figure for me. My thanks are also due to Dr. John H. Hanks and

Dr. Don Fawcett for permission to quote from or paraphrase sections of their mimeographed laboratory outline. With the above exceptions, the illustrations are all drawn or prepared by me. Pictures taken from periodicals or from older books carry their specific acknowledgments. The bibliography at the end of the book is intended to cover only those papers directly relevant to the text. For collateral material the reader should refer to the *Tissue Culture Bibliography* published under the auspices of the Tissue Culture Association.

P. R. W.

CONTENTS

xi

THE CULTIVATION OF
ANIMAL AND PLANT CELLS

"MAN KANN sich also folgende zwei Vorstellungen von der Ursache der organischen Erscheinungen, des Wachstum usw. machen: Erstens die Ursache liegt in der Totalität des Organismus. . . . Die andere Erklärungsweise ist die: Das Wachstum geschieht nicht durch eine im ganzen Organismus begrundete Kraft, sondern jeder einzeine Elementarteil besitzt eine selbständige Kraft, ein selbständiges Leben. . . .

"Wir haben gesehen, dass alle Organismen aus wesentlich gleichen Teilen, nämlich aus Zellen zusammengesetzt sind, dass diese Zellen nach wesentlich denselben Gesetzen sich bilden und wachsen, dass also diese Prozesse überall auch durch dieselben Kräfte hervorgebracht werden müssen. Finden wir nun, dass einzelne dieser Elementarteile . . . sich vom Organismus lostrennen und selbständig weiter wachsen können, so können wir daraus schliessen, dass auch jeder der übrigen Elementarteile, jede Zelle, . . . selbständig sich zu entwickeln imstande wäre, wenn ihm bloss die äusseren Bedingungen dargeboten würden, unter welchen er im Organismus steht. Solche selbständig, getrennt vom Organismus wachsende Zellen sind z. B. die Eier der Tiere. . . . Bei niederen Pflanzen kann sich jede beliebige Zelle von der Pflanze lostrennen und dann selbständig weiter wachsen. . . . So müssen wir überhaupt den Zellen ein selbständiges Leben zuschreiben . . . Dass nicht wirklich jede einzelne Zelle, wenn sie von einem Organismus getrennt wird, weiter wächst, ist gegen diese Theorie so wenig ein Einwurf, als es ein Einwurf gegen das selbständige Leben einer Biene ist, wenn sie getrennt von ihrem Schwarm auf die Dauer nicht fortbestehen kann."

THEODORE SCHWANN (1839), pp. 188–90.

✿   ✿   ✿

"ONE CAN thus construct the following two hypotheses concerning the origin of organic phenomena such as growth: either this origin is a function of the organism as a whole—or growth does not take place by means of any force residing in the entire organism, but each elementary part possesses an individual force, a separate life.

"We have seen that all organisms consist of essentially like parts, the cells; that these cells are formed and grow according to essentially the same laws; that these processes are thus everywhere the result of the same forces. If, therefore, we find that some of these elementary parts . . . are capable of being separated from the organism and of continuing to grow independently, we can conclude that each of the other elementary parts, each cell, . . . would be capable of developing independently if only there be provided the external conditions under which it exists in the organism. The eggs of animals are in fact such cells, capable of living separated from the organism. Among the lower plants any cell can be separated from the plant and continue to grow. . . . We must therefore ascribe an independent life to the cell as such. That not every cell grows, when separated from the organism, is no more an argument against this theory than is the fact that a bee soon dies when separated from its swarm a valid argument against the individual life of the bee."

Chapter 1

THE CELL VERSUS
THE ORGANISM

I N THE whole range of human thought there is perhaps no
single question more frequently and variously posed than
this: "By what means do the myriads of different forms and
processes which we see in the Universe around us come into
being? What controls these forms and processes within
normal metes and bounds, and how does it come about that
those 'normal' bounds are occasionally transcended, so often
with disastrous results? What is it that brings about and
maintains the extraordinary harmony which we find in nature, yet from time to time alters that harmony by what appear to us to be transgressions?" Our search for answers to
the multitudinous variants of this great question is unending.

For this question does have a multitude of variants. It is
asked at all levels of human experience. At the cosmic level
it becomes the question of creation itself. The psychologist
asks it at the level of human thought and behavior. The so-
ciologist asks it at the level of races and nations, tribes, sects,
and societies. The chemist asks it at the level of "substances,"
and the physicist asks it at the level of material bodies, great
or small, be they galaxies, or atoms, or particles of light. The
geneticist and the taxonomist ask it concerning the segregation and delimitation of characters of related organisms.
With regard to single organisms we ask, how is it that the
size, form, texture, rate of development, and function of the
various parts are determined and limited? Why does an

3

anterior limb bud give rise to a hand while a posterior limb bud gives rise to a foot? Why does a cell of one type, when chance places it in one region of the body, become an element of the glandular epithelium of the kidney, while in another part of the body the same type of cell becomes a nerve, and in a third appears as a constituent of the iris? Why does the subepidermal cell of a foliar leaf become a center of food synthesis, while in a floral leaf it becomes a megaspore mother cell with a reproductive function? Why do the cells surrounding a wound in a "normal" individual take part in an orderly granulation, closing the wound, forming well-limited scar tissue, organizing a harmonious replacement of the injured regions, while in an individual carrying a cancer, even at some distant part of the body, cells of the same region may be detonated into an explosive, disordered, disharmonious, and ultimately self-destroying overgrowth? The factors which control these characteristics of size, form, function, and rate of development of living organisms, which maintain at all times the proper balance among their parts, and which, when disturbed, result in creatures of abnormal type, constitute the materials of that important branch of biological science which we call "morphogenesis."

Science progresses in five main steps. First, there is the observation of more or less evident facts, their codification, and analysis. After that comes the formulation of ideas and general principles based on these facts, and their arrangement into working hypotheses. Third, there is the development of techniques for testing these hypotheses. Fourth is the acquiring, through the use of these techniques, of pertinent but less evident information, and the verification, modification, and refinement of these hypotheses until they themselves become facts. And fifth, there is the integration of these latterly acquired facts into the general picture.

The discipline of cell culture exemplifies beautifully these five steps. As a segment of biological thought, the foundations of cell culture are very ancient indeed. In the fourth century before Christ, Theophrastus (320 B.C.) [1] and Aristotle (360 B.C.) described plants and animals as being made up of certain homogeneous elements, sap and blood, fiber and flesh, nerves and veins, wood and bone. But, having no lenses for closer examination, they were unable to give more definite descriptions of the structure of these elements. Two millennia later, with the development of the microscope, Hooke (1667) showed that what Theophrastus had called "fiber" and Aristotle "bone" were made up of smaller homogeneous units. These he called "cells." A century and a half later Brown (1828) recognized the ubiquity of "nuclei" in fleshy as well as in fibrous or bony materials, especially of plants, and Dujardin (1835) noted that the semi-fluid substance which commonly covers the cellular skeleton in the living parts of plants and animals has also an ubiquitous and hence evidently important role. This covering he called the "sarcode," the forerunner of our protoplasm (note that I do not say "protoplast"). These three concepts, of the ubiquity of the (lifeless) "cell" of Hooke, of the "nucleus" of Brown, and of the "sarcode" of Dujardin, were crystallized in 1838 in the cell theory jointly formulated by Schleiden (1838), a botanist, and Schwann (1839), a zoologist.

But if we are to understand the nature, aims, and methods of cell culture and their significance, we must remember that the "cell theory" had two distinct aspects. In the first place it recognized that the compartmentalization which Hooke had seen in dead materials (cork, pith, etc.) was a universal phenomenon in all or nearly all parts of both plants and animals, and that therefore the cell was a universal structural unit of all living creatures. This aspect of the theory was quickly accepted and has become an unconscious part of all our thinking. In the second place, however, it clearly stated a corollary which has by no means received universal

[1] References are to the bibliography at the end of this volume.

acceptance; namely, that these ubiquitous structural units are also distinct physiological and developmental units, capable of separate existence under certain conditions, with the same sort of individuality, in the words of Schwann (1839), as have the individual bees in a hive. The idea that each cell is an individual capable of autonomous existence, and that an "animal" or "plant" is no more than a "society" of cooperating cells, has by no means received general acceptance.

For there is an alternative hypothesis which also rests upon a considerable mass of observed facts; namely, that somewhere in the developmental history of an organism, its constituent cells cease to be totipotent, by segregation and loss of certain capacities. No mechanism is known by which such segregation or loss can take place unless it is the variation in chromosome numbers among different organs reported by Hsu [2] but as yet unconfirmed, yet segregation of potencies so often appears to have taken place that this alternative hypothesis, which demands emphasis on "the organism as a whole," has today many adherents. Sharp (1926) has presented these views in excellent fashion. I particularly recommend his introductory chapter and the papers of Baker (1951, 1952). They deserve careful reading.

If all cells of an organism are essentially alike and, within the genetic pattern, totipotent, then the differences in behavior of cells of a given type in different situations in the body must result from the interrelations of those cells with their environment and with other cells in the organism. It should be possible to restore suppressed functions by isolating the cell from those external influences which were responsible for the suppression. If, on the other hand, there has been a true segregation and loss of function so that the cells, in the mature organism, are no longer totipotent, then no modification of a given cell-line's environment could hope

[2] Personal communication.

to restore the lost functions. It is clear that a decision between these two alternative hypotheses is essential to any valid concept of the origin of form and function. And it is also clear that one of the most promising techniques for arriving at such a decision lies in the segregation of cells, tissues, and organs from the associated members of the body, and their maintenance and study as isolated units under as nearly optimal and as fully controlled conditions as possible. The attempt to reduce an organism to its constituent cells and to study these cells as elementary organisms is thus a project of fundamental importance in the solution of basic biological questions. This is the problem of cell culture.

Nevertheless, most of our biological thinking and experimentation today completely ignores the concept of physiological cellular autonomy. The histologist and anatomist consider the *tissue* rather than the *cell* as the important unit; the cytologist is chiefly interested in *internal* cellular members (mitochondria, microsomes, nuclei, chromomeres); the physiologist and endocrinologist study "systems" (the nervous system, the digestive system, the respiratory system); and even the biochemist is interested in chemical systems (cytochrome, the Krebs cycle, the extracellular digestive juices). We still think in terms of heart action, kidney function, muscle contraction, and blood circulation—that is, in terms of *organ* function; or at the other extreme, we think of pancreatic juice digestion, visual purple, cytochrome, and insulin—that is, in terms of chemical processes which we study outside the cell. In none of these are we thinking in terms of the cell itself. Yet, when a gland secretes pituitrin it is the cell which is carrying on the physiological process, not the gland; when a nerve carries a stimulus it is the nerve cell which performs the conduction, not the complex system which we call a "nerve"; when a muscle contracts it is the individual cells which carry out the physicochemical changes responsible for contraction; when a "tissue" respires it is the individual cells which carry on the process. The tissues and organs are merely means of integrating the varied activities of the constituent cells into a machine which can function. True, this integration is essential for the normal functioning of the organism as a whole, but it is not essential for the normal functioning of the individual parts, the cells.

It seems strange that this fact has not really penetrated below the surface of our thinking. Many workers, particularly a half century ago, recognized clearly the individuality of the cell. Verworn (1895, p. 53) stated, "It is to the cell that the study of every bodily function sooner or later drives us. In the muscle cell lies the problem of the heart beat and of muscular contraction; in the gland cell resides the cause of secretion; in the epithelial cell, in the white blood corpuscle, lies the problem of the absorption of food, and the secrets of the mind are hidden in the ganglion cell."

Yet the idea has not "stuck" (White, 1948). Where will you find such statements in modern physiology texts? Whitman in 1893 and in still more emphatic terms Conklin in 1940 maintained that the theory of cellular autonomy is inadequate to explain development and should be set aside. Sharp, too (1926), leans strongly toward the organism as being the important unit rather than the cell. To them the cell is no more than a structural means of integrating the functions of an organism. If, as is true in medical philosophy, the well integrated organism is the only proper final objective of all study, then perhaps they are right. They have many followers. The concept of organs, systems, and the "organism as a whole" dominates the scene.

Yet both philosophy and science have had to face the fact that in practice integration must follow dissection, not precede it. Man's mind lacks the omniscience to grasp these matters "as a whole." Much as we might like to study only integrated wholes we recognize when we face facts, not fancies, that it is impractical to try to do so. The concept of the cell as an elementary functional unit is a very practical concept. Because it is practical it has had sufficient vitality to reappear repeatedly in spite of neglect and of all that has been said against it. Claude Bernard's emphasis on the "internal environment" (1872, 1878) was an attempt to formulate an ecology of these units. It is from Schleiden and Schwann, through Bernard, that we must trace the origins of cell culture.

"Es SIND meines Wissens nach bisher noch keine planmässig angelegten Versuche gemacht worden, isolierte vegetative Zellen von höher entwickelten Pflanzen in geeigneten Nährlösungen zu kultivieren. Und doch müssten die Ergebnisse solcher Kulturversuche manches interessante Streiflicht auf die Eigenschaften und Fähigkeiten werfen die die Zelle als Elementarorganismus in sich birgt: sie müssten Aufschlüsse bringen über die Wechselbeziehungen und gegenseitigen Beeinflüssungen denen die Zellen innerhalb des vielzelligen Gesamtorganismus ausgesetzt sind."

G. HABERLANDT (1902), p. 69.

✿   ✿   ✿

"THERE has been, so far as I know, up to the present, no planned attempt to cultivate the vegetative cells of higher plants in suitable nutrients. Yet the results of such attempts should cast many interesting sidelights on the peculiarities and capacities which the cell, as an elementary organism, possesses. They should make possible, conclusions as to the interrelations and reciprocal influences to which the cell is subjected within the multicellular organism."

Chapter 2

THE HISTORY OF
CELL CULTURE

FROM the historical point of view the subject of cell culture may be divided into two preliminary and three
experimental stages (Fig. 1). The first, previous to 1839,
we have already mentioned. The second stage, from 1839
to 1902, was likewise a relatively inactive phase. Neither
Schleiden and Schwann, who formulated the concept of cellular totipotency, nor Virchow (1858), the medical pathol-
ogist who popularized that concept, made any attempt to
put it to experimental test. Nor did Claude Bernard, who
formulated the complementary concept of the "internal environment" through which the effects which one cell exerts
upon another (and particularly upon distant cells) are considered to be mediated, carry out any experiments which
might settle the question.

A half century elapsed between the first clear expression
of the concept and the first well organized experimental
study of the matter. In the 1870's several workers attacked
the problem, no one with more lucidity and patience than
Vöchting (1878). Vöchting chose two methods of approach.
First he dissected plants into smaller and smaller fragments,
studying the phenomena of polarity in these fragments
(1878, 1884, 1892). He found "polarity" to be a characteristic of every fragment, irrespective of size, and by extrapo-
lation probably of the individual cells. Thus the distal portion of a stem always produced leaves and the proximal por-

11

tion roots, but whether a given cell produced leaves or roots depended on that cell's fortuitous position, whether distal or proximal to the nearest cut surface or uninjured growing point. If a 3-foot piece of willow was left intact, the distal foot of stem would produce only roots, but if a 6-inch piece

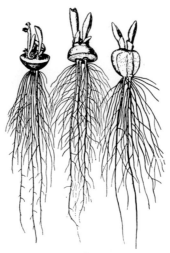

FIGURE 2. Tubers of *Corydalis solida,* cut in two perpendicular planes and allowed to regenerate. The cells at the center of the tuber, which in an intact plant serve only for the storage of food, have produced three distinct kinds of members: leaves (left), roots (center), or merely wound callus (right), depending on their spatial relationships to the plane of the cut; this shows the dependence of morphogenetic expression on fortuitous external factors. (From Goebel, 1908, p. 220, Fig. 111. Compare with Fig. 4.)

was isolated from this same distal end of stem, either by removal or merely by severing the bark, the proximal 3 inches of this piece would produce leaves instead of roots. Here the morphogenetic pattern is a function of the "organism as a whole" (considering here the autonomous fragment as the organism), of the relation of cell to cell within the particular tissue continuum. The cell appears to be totipotent, its actual expression being a resultant of the influences coming from outside (Fig. 2). With animals this approach was developed a generation later by Child, whose "axial gradients" are quite comparable to Vöchting's concepts of polarity.

Vöchting's second approach involved the age-old methods of grafting and transplantation (1892). These studies gave striking additional evidence of tissue polarities and cellular autonomy. They also confirmed what had been known from time immemorial, that no matter what the environment or host into which a scion was transplanted, it always developed in a pattern which was fixed by the species from which it came (Fig. 3). Not only was the developmental pattern

FIGURE 3. (Left) Ovary segments of three varieties of gourds (*à fruits jaunes*, above; *poire verte*, center; *à fruits blancs*, below) grafted together. Each variety retains its specific characteristics, although in intimate anatomical and physiological contact with the tissues of other varieties. The portion *à fruits blanc* must obtain all its nutriment, both from the soil and from the leaves, through the tissues of two other varieties, yet its character remains unaffected by this fact. The dependence of morphogenetic capacity on strictly hereditary, internal factors is clearly shown. (From E. A. Carrière, 1875)

(Right) A comparable example drawn from animal morphogenesis. Segments of larvae of *Rana palustris*, light in color, and of *R. sylvatica*, with dark pigmentation, have been grafted together in the early embryonic stages. Each retains its own specific characteristics in intimate anatomical and physiological contact with the other. (From R. G. Harrison, 1904)

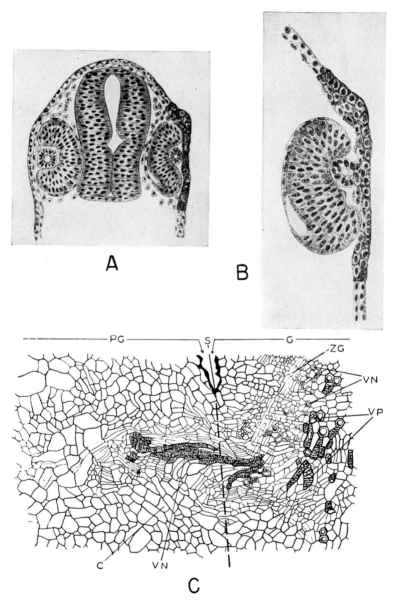

A

B

C

FIGURE 4A, B. Results of grafting belly epithelium of a toad embryo (*Bufo vulgaris*) onto the eye region of an embryo of a frog (*Rana esculenta*). Here the grafted epithelium has formed, owing to its spatial relationship to

14

fixed, but the physiological behavior was also fixed by the species and could not be altered by contact with or even dependence on the tissues of another species (Carrière, 1875; Vöchting, 1892, 1894; Harrison, 1904). The transplantation experiments demonstrated the restrictions which species places on the potencies of a cell (Fig. 3). The dissection experiments demonstrated the essential totipotency of the cell within these species limitations (Figs. 2, 4). Similar transplantations were studied with animal materials, again a generation later, by Spemann and his followers (1936), with results of similar import and of the greatest importance for our understanding of embryonic morphogenesis.

Dissection and isolation were carried a step further by Roux (1885), who isolated the chick medullary plate and kept it alive for some days in saline solution in an effort to determine the factors involved in the closure of the medullary tube. In 1887 Arnold "cultivated" leucocytes by an ingenious method.[1] He soaked very thin slices of alder pith in aqueous humor of the frog. These were then implanted under the skin or in the peritoneal cavity of frogs, where they were soon invaded by leucocytes. He then removed the slices of pith at intervals and put them into a dish of

---

[1] I am indebted to Dr. Arthur Hughes of the Department of Anatomy, Cambridge University, for this very interesting and important reference, which so far as I know does not appear in any of the standard tissue culture reviews. Arnold seems to have anticipated by decades the studies of Leo Loeb, Speidel, Algire, and many others.

---

the eye-cup of the host, a lens. Since eyes are never normally present in the belly of the toad, this result shows that belly epithelium possesses a potency (the lens-forming potency) which, while never normally expressed, can be evoked by suitable circumstances. The species characteristics of the transplant (melanotic pigmentation) have been determined by the source, while the morphological characteristics have been determined by the host. A, Cross section of the entire head region. B, Detail of the right-hand eye showing the transplant. (From Filatow, 1925.) C, Result of grafting a bud of *Scorzonera* into a pith culture of the same plant. The graft (at the right) has induced the formation of a vascular strand (VN) extending across the line of suture (S) into the normally parenchymatous, undifferentiated tissue of the host (PG). (From Camus, 1929, Fig. 60A)

saline solution or of aqueous humor and observed that the leucocytes migrated from the pith into the saline solution, where they survived for some time (1887). He studied their mitotic divisions, made drawings of many types of cells, and clearly demonstrated their individuality and partial independence. Ljunggren (1898) maintained bits of skin alive in ascitic fluid. Jolly likewise kept leucocytes alive in serum (1903). These were, however, with the possible exception of Arnold's work, little more than brief technical tours de force, without intended or implied general biological significance. Somewhat closer to the main stream of cell culture and very similar to Arnold's studies was the work of Leo Loeb (1902), who followed the progressive migration of cells into a blood clot or block of gelatine implanted either in the ear of a rabbit or intraperitoneally. This was essentially an internal and hence rather unmanageable type of "tissue culture."

To carry Vöchting's type of dissection to its logical end, we would have to go to the cells themselves as, indeed, Arnold, Jolly, and Loeb had done. But the idea of cultivating single isolated body cells *in vitro* as a general biological problem seems not to have been explicitly formulated until 1902. In that year Haberlandt, a botanist, set forth the problem frankly and lucidly in the words which stand at the head of this chapter. The discipline which he thus outlined is that which, in the half century since his paper, has gradually crystallized into what we know today as "tissue culture," or, as I prefer to call it, "cell culture." Our third period begins with this paper.

But it is not always given to one individual to formulate the broad outlines of a new technique and also to put that technique into actual practice. Where Vöchting (1878, 1884, 1892) and after him Rechinger (1893) had sought to determine the "limits of divisibility" of plant materials, Haberlandt (1902) boldly took his point of departure directly from the cell theory and assumed that there were no limits of divisibility. He therefore chose to work with single cells, an aim which we now look upon as having been an elusive ideal, at least in his day. It has only recently been attained with animal cells by Sanford, Earle, and Likely (1948); similar reports for plant cells are still uncorroborated (Schmucker, 1929; Northcraft, 1951).

Haberlandt, fully appreciating the importance of the photosynthetic process for all living material, conceived the idea that the cultivation of green cells would eliminate the need to provide carbohydrate in the nutrient. In this he apparently lost sight of the fact that green cells are relatively mature and highly differentiated units which have, to a great extent, lost their meristematic function. Haberlandt was, moreover, faced with a number of difficulties which are inherent in plant anatomy and morphogenesis. In the first place, most cells of a plant are not bathed in any free, complete nutrient medium. The xylem sap, although rich in inorganic salts, lacks many of the organic constituents needed to maintain life. The phloem sap, which contains elaborated organic materials, is in direct contact with only a very few specialized cells. Most plant cells must obtain the greater part of their nutriment by diffusion *through* neighboring cells. There is no "natural" nutrient which can be extracted from a plant and used for the cultivation of its cells and for subsequent analysis, except the liquid endosperms which do not exist at all in most plants. Where they do exist, they are usually present only in minute amounts. An exception is the coconut milk recently introduced with some success as a nutrient for plant cell cultures. In the second place, most plant cells, with rare exceptions, are surrounded by a rigid pellicle of cellulose. This prevents the cells from seeking and engulfing food, thus greatly restricting the forms of food which they can use. It prevents their adhering satisfactorily to any solid substratum. And, since excision involves rupturing this pellicle and exposing the protoplast naked to the surrounding medium in a way that seldom occurs in nature, there results a considerable and unavoidable shock. In the third place "growth" in the plant is normally restricted to a few specialized regions of the body, leaving all other parts in a relatively inert or at least dormant condition as far as capacity for immediate cell division is concerned, and thereby greatly restricting the experimenter in his choice of materials.

As a result of these inherent difficulties all of Haberlandt's attempts and those of his immediate successors to cultivate plant cells *in vitro* were, without exception, disappointing. The attempt to attack the problem directly was regretfully abandoned with the remark that "Jedenfalls dürfte die Methode der Züchtung isolierter Zellen in Nährlösungen verschiedene wichtige Probleme von einer neuen Seite her der experimentellen Bearbeitung zugänglich machen" (1902). (At any rate, the cultivation of isolated cells in nutrient solutions should make possible an experimental approach to many important problems from a new point of view.) Haberlandt turned to an indirect approach, that of the study of wound healing, and never personally returned to the original problem.

Fortunately for the development of the field as a whole, however, animal tissues present none of the above-named difficulties, at least to anything like a comparable degree. In the first place animal cells throughout the body *are* regularly bathed in one of three characteristic and essentially complete nutrient fluids—the blood, interstitial fluid, and lymph. These can be easily removed from the body in considerable quantity. They serve as basic "natural" nutrients for animal cells in which such cells can be immersed without serious shock. They can be analyzed at leisure to determine which of their constituents are truly essential. In the second place animal cells are, for the most part, surrounded by a tough but mobile pellicle in place of the semi-rigid pellicle of the plant cell. Animal cells can therefore be removed from the body with a minimum of shock; anyone who has worked with both types will appreciate this difference. Animal cells adhere well to a variety of solid substrata. They are capable of autonomous movement and phagocytosis, so that they can be fed on relatively complex nutrient materials which they themselves transform into constituents which can pass readily into the protoplasts. And finally, "growth" regularly takes place in all parts of the animal body and, in the sense of replacement, occurs throughout the life of the animal. There is thus comparatively little obvious restriction placed on the experimenter in choosing favorable materials for cultivation. These facts have largely affected the progress of cell culture in the two living kingdoms. As a result, progress passed in the first decade of this century entirely into the hands of the zoologists.

The transition is a noteworthy one. At about the same time that Haberlandt was formulating the concept of cell and tissue cultures, a controversy was raging among zoologists as to whether the fibrillae observed in histological preparations, which connect the neurocenters with their end-organs, originate from the nerve cell, from the end-organ, or from the intervening ground substance. A considerable body of opinion supported an origin *de novo* from the ground substance. This view was held by the great German anatomist, Hensen. Ramon y Cajal and His were the chief proponents of an origin by outgrowth from the neurone. Classic histology had proved itself incompetent to settle the matter. Harrison had tried transplanting the neural crest to various parts of the body, without arriving at a definite answer. Turning then to the methods suggested by Haberlandt and tested cursorily by Arnold, Roux, Ljunggren, and Jolly, Harrison in 1907 settled the controversy in two now classic papers (1907, 1910). He cultivated the neuroblast of the frog in

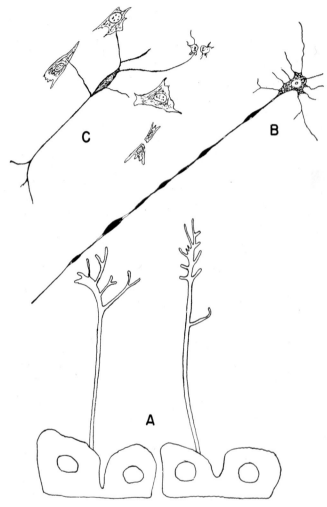

FIGURE 5. A, Neuroblast of the frog, grown in clotted lymph. Two drawings of a single nerve fiber, drawn 50 minutes apart to show the extensive
changes in outline which such a growing fiber undergoes. Excepting
Arnold's 1887 figure, this is probably the oldest picture of a growing meta-
zoan cell, in culture. (From Harrison, 1908, Fig. 22.) B, Sympathetic
nerve of chick-embryo intestine, cultivated in saline solution directly on
glass, without a clot. This drawing is from a fixed and stained preparation.
(From M. R. Lewis and W. H. Lewis, 1912a, Fig. 23.) C, Human brain

clotted lymph and observed the growth of the fibrillae from the central body (Fig. 5). This was the first successful "tissue culture." Harrison followed the presentation of his experimental results with a brilliant exposé of the possibilities of this method of approach (1912); but he had devised the method only to solve a particular problem, and once this was done he made no attempt to develop it further. Two years later Burrows studied with Harrison and introduced the idea of substituting blood plasma for lymph in the cultivation of chick cells (1910a, b; 1911). He also appears to have coined the term "tissue culture." He subsequently joined Carrel, and together these two developed the use of embryo juice as a growth-promoting nutrient and elaborated the methods for growing a great variety of animal tissues (Carrel, 1912, 1913b, c). These methods, with minor modifications, remained standard for the next thirty years and are still widely used (Carrel, 1924; Harrison, 1928).

The methods introduced by Harrison, Burrows and Carrel, and their lineal followers, the cultivation of animal cells in a blood-plasma embryo-juice nutrient, are relatively simple and easily duplicated. They have not, however, led to any exact knowledge of the nutrient requirements of such cells and tissues. Blood plasma and embryo juice are organic complexes of unknown composition. Attempts to analyze these complexes have, it is true, been made from time to time over the intervening years by Ebeling (1921a, b), Carrel and Baker (1926), Fischer and Demuth (1928), Drew (1923), and others. Although one may find in the literature many important studies of this sort, and not a few which come as a surprise to one steeped in present-day thought in

cell cultivated on a plasma-coated cover glass insert in a roller-tube culture. A fixed and stained preparation. (Redrawn from I. Costero and C. M. Pomerat, 1951, Fig. 17.) The similarity in pattern between the cells of frog, chick, and human, grown under modern and under earlier conditions, is evident.

FIGURE 6. The Founders of Cell Culture, 1902–1952.

the field, these studies have had little effect on subsequent work and to an extraordinary extent have been forgotten.

At about the same time that Carrel was beginning his work (1912), Warren and Margaret Lewis, likewise under Harrison's influence, began a careful study of the effects of individual nutrient constituents. The effects of salts, carbohydrates, total osmotic value, and similar factors, on the short-term growth of animal cells *in vitro* were investigated (M. R. Lewis and W. H. Lewis, 1911a, b; 1912a, b). This approach, while less productive of immediate spectacular results in terms of prolonged growth and observable differences in developmental pattern, was, in theory, more likely to lead to an ultimate understanding of the physiological processes involved. In the absence of information on the roles or even the existence of many of the vitamins, amino acids, respiratory intermediates, enzymes, and the like, it was ahead of its time and did not then lead to important results. It forms the point of departure, however, for much more recent work.

For the next decade, from 1910 to 1920, "tissue culture" consisted largely of a survey to determine how many "tis-

←

Gottlieb Haberlandt, 1854–1946, Director, Pflanzenphysiologisches Institut, the University of Berlin, Germany. First to formulate, in clear fashion, the idea of cultivating isolated cells *in vitro* as a method of studying problems of organization and cellular interrelationships. First to make planned studies of the cultivation of cells.

Ross G. Harrison, 1870– , Professor Emeritus, Osborn Zoological Laboratory, Yale University, New Haven, Connecticut. First successfully to cultivate isolated cells as a means of solving a specific morphogenetic problem.

Alexis Carrel, 1873–1945, Member, The Rockefeller Institute for Medical Research, New York City. Responsible, more than any other individual, for developing and perfecting the techniques of cell culture.

Albert Fischer, 1891– , Director, Biological Laboratories of the Carlsberg Foundation, Copenhagen, Denmark. Chief European proponent of the cell culture method as developed by Carrel.

Warren H. Lewis, 1870– , and *Margaret R. Lewis*, 1881– , Emeritus Associates, the Carnegie Laboratory of Embryology, Johns Hopkins School of Medicine, Baltimore, Maryland. First to study in detail problems of cellular nutrition *in vitro*.

sues" of how many different animals could be grown for more or less prolonged periods. This has continued, but about 1920 a number of other approaches began to develop. In 1923 the introduction of the Carrel flask in place of the hanging drop (Carrel, 1923a, b) greatly reduced the amount of routine work required to maintain strains and to grow appreciable masses of tissue. It also permitted a more quantitative approach to many of the problems involved. One natural consequence of this improvement in technique was the opening up of the possibility of studying nutritional problems. This was undertaken by Carrel and his co-workers, Ebeling and Baker. By analyzing tissue juices by simple methods such as filtration, dialysis, precipitation, and differential extraction, these workers made a number of important contributions in this direction between 1923 and 1939 (Baker and Carrel, 1926, 1928; Baker, 1936; Baker and Ebeling, 1939), when Carrel retired and his laboratory was disbanded. It has been continued by Carrel's former collaborator, Fischer, in Denmark, and has recently been taken up again by a number of workers, especially Barski in Paris (Barski, Maurin, Wielgosz, and Lépine, 1951) and Harris in California (1952a, b).

At about the same time that the development of the Carrel flask gave a powerful impetus to cell culture studies on animal materials, work was renewed in the parallel plant field which, in spite of the efforts of a series of Haberlandt's students—Bobilioff-Preisser, Lamprecht, Thielman, Czech, Börger, and others—had remained no more of a reality than it had been in the days of Haberlandt's brilliant theoretical exposé of twenty years before (1902). In 1921 Molliard (1921) attempted with some success to cultivate fragments of plant embryos. He dropped the work and it was not resumed until 1934, in the hands of Gautheret (1934, see below). In 1922 Kotte (1922), a student of Haberlandt, and independently Robbins (1922a, b) in the United States, succeeded in growing excised plant roots for some weeks in a nutrient solution. Kotte dropped the work, but Robbins, with a co-worker, Maneval, published two more papers in the next two years which showed clearly that considerable growth, but apparently not indefinite growth, of certain roots could be obtained, and outlined some of the conditions necessary therefor (Robbins and Maneval, 1923, 1924). Robbins too turned to other fields and did not return to this one for twelve years (Robbins, V. B. White, McClary, and Bartley, 1936).

It was not until 1934 that the field of plant tissue culture was definitely opened by two workers, White and Gautheret. White had surveyed the past history of the field in 1931, and had pointed out some of the probable reasons for earlier failures and the directions which future work might profitably take (White, 1931). He had emphasized the suitability of the Kotte-Robbins root-tip method for study of the nutritional aspects of the problem, and had called attention to the theoretical weakness of Haberlandt's earlier approach and to difficulties in the way of obtaining results by means of Molliard's method. This theoretical discussion was followed by a series of factual papers presenting experiments with excised root tips, which culminated in 1934 in the demonstration of the possibility of growing excised roots of tomato *in vitro* for periods which had no theoretical limit (White, 1934a). These were the first successful "tissue" cultures (or perhaps better, "organ cultures") of plant material. The roots started at that time are still growing today, after twenty years and more than 1,000 passages.

In the same year Gautheret, under the direction of the great French cytologist, Guilliermond, and influenced by Molliard's earlier work and White's 1931 discussion, after making somewhat less successful experiments with root tips than those of White, turned to an intensive study of the cultivation of cambial tissues, beginning with those of willow and poplar (Gautheret, 1934, 1935, 1937, 1938a, b).

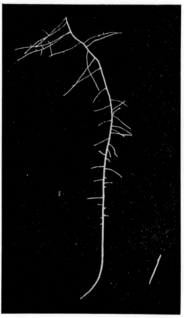

FIGURE 7. An isolated root of tomato grown *in vitro*. At the right, a piece about a centimeter long used as inoculum; at the left, a similar piece after ten days' growth. The photograph was taken after one year of cultivation. This same strain is still alive after twenty years and more than 1,000 passages, and is still growing at a rate of about a centimeter per culture per day. (From White, 1934a)

These at first proved refractory. Their study was continued, however,[2] and in 1939 Gautheret (1939) in Paris,

[2] There is a story connected with Gautheret's doctorate which is worth repeating for the light which it throws on those traits which characterize and mold a great scientist. Roger Gautheret was the only son of a well-to-do French business man and as such was in a position to indulge his own wishes to a considerable degree. After he had completed his "Licenciate," he went to Prof. Guilliermond, under whom he intended to take his doctorate, and said to him, "My Professor, I want to take a doctorate under your direction. I have both money and time. I do not need a position. I can devote all my time to research. I do not care how long it takes to get

Nobécourt (1937, 1939a) in Grenoble, and White (1939a) in Princeton published independently within a period of six weeks descriptions of the successful cultivation for prolonged periods of cambial tissues of tobacco and carrot. These were the first true plant tissue cultures in the strict sense of prolonged cultures of unorganized materials. To-

FIGURE 8.   One of Gautheret's cultures of carrot tissue.   This culture is about two months old and is representative of a strain which has been in cultivation since 1937.   (From Gautheret, 1948b, Fig. 3)

gether with White's earlier studies on root nutrition, these papers are to plant tissue culture what the papers of Harrison in 1907, Burrows in 1910, and Carrel in 1910–1913 were to the animal field. They have led to the work of White and Braun (1942) on the cultivation of sterile crown-gall tissue, which has opened up the field of experimental study of plant

my degree, or how much it costs, but I do want it to be worth something. What problem can you suggest which would really be worth while?" Prof. Guilliermond gave him two problems, one of them the cultivation of plant tissues. Gautheret accepted the challenge with enthusiasm. The first years were years of frustration for both. When positive results finally began to emerge, both were grateful—the pupil for having a master who could formulate such far-reaching and important goals, and the master for having found so tenacious and brilliant a student!

FIGURE 9. Some Present-Day Tissue Culture Leaders.

cancers, to Gautheret's studies on "habituation" of tissues to growth substances (1942b, 1946, 1947a, b, 1948a), to the studies of Blakeslee on plant embryos (van Overbeek, Conklin, and Blakeslee, 1941, 1942), to the work of deRopp (1947, 1948), and others.

Parallel with these there was developing independently a quite different type of investigation introduced by Fell (1928a, b, 1931) in England, in which whole embryonic "organules" (Fischer's term, 1922) such as bones, teeth, eyes, and glands were grown in relatively large volumes of nutrient in simple watch glasses and their metabolism studied. This is comparable in many ways to White's root cultures. It is an important approach, quite different from Carrel's single-tissue pure-line studies or the technically complex cultures of entire adult organs, begun by Carrel as early as 1906 (1913a) and perfected by Carrel and Lindbergh in 1938. Because of its technical complexities, the Carrel-Lindbergh approach, while spectacular, has never established itself as a working method and has contributed little to

←——————————————————————————————

Honor B. Fell, 1900– , Director, the Strangeways Research Laboratory, Cambridge, England. Investigator of the *in vitro* development and function of animal organs.

Margaret R. Murray, 1901– , Professor of Surgery, College of Physicians and Surgeons, Columbia University Medical Center, New York City. Responsible director, the *Tissue Culture Bibliography* (1953); developed the use of cell cultures in the classification and diagnosis of tumors, particularly neuromas.

Roger J. Gautheret, 1910– , Professeur de Botanique, the Sorbonne, Paris. First to cultivate normal plant tissues *in vitro*. Founder of the European school of plant tissue culture.

Philip R. White, 1901– , Research Associate, the Roscoe B. Jackson Memorial Laboratory, Bar Harbor, Maine. First to establish continuous cultures of plant organs and of plant tumor tissues. First to develop fully defined maintenance nutrients for both plant and animal cells.

Wilton R. Earle, 1902– , Principal Cytologist, the National Cancer Institute, Bethesda, Md. Developed quantitative methods for the maintenance and study of animal cell cultures.

George O. Gey, 1899– , Assistant Professor of Surgery, Johns Hopkins School of Medicine, Baltimore, Md. Developed the roller-tube method for simple cell cultures of animal cells.

our knowledge other than the demonstration of the possibility of maintaining such organs *in vitro* for long periods, while the much simpler, more direct method of Fell has, in her hands and in the hands of Gaillard (1948) and others, contributed a great deal of valuable information (Martinovitch, 1938, 1950; Carpenter, 1942).

With Carrel's retirement in 1939, his group scattered and his school of tissue culture was no longer active. This was partly because its emphasis on technical niceties had prevented the accumulation of any large group of neophytes. As early as 1930 the field had already begun to pass into the hands of others with different points of view. In 1933 Gey (1933, 1936), working with Lewis (1934), introduced the first practical roller-tube method (see below) as a substitute for the Carrel flask. This, as we shall see, is much less expensive, technically much simpler, and equally effective for many purposes. Gey's personal approach has continued to be that of developing methods and maintaining many strains for observation of their spontaneous behavior, rather than that of extensive experiment. Most of the experimental results of this very important method have come from other laboratories (however, see Ehrmann and Gey, 1953).

In 1943 White, who with Gautheret and others had in the previous decade brought the question of the nutrition of excised plant tissues to a fairly high level of precision, turned his attention to corresponding problems in the handling of animal tissues. He adopted the techniques of Gey, the type of thinking which had motivated the Lewises thirty years before, and the factual background contributed by the heterogeneous accumulation of recent rapid advances in the understanding of such substances as vitamins, protein constituents, respiratory intermediates, enzymes, and trace-element catalysts in their bearing on the nutrition of microorganisms and of higher animals, including man. On this basis he developed a tentative synthetic nutrient capable of supporting prolonged survival of animal tissue cultures (1946, 1949) without significant growth. At about the same time Fischer (1941a, b), with somewhat the same general aim in mind but by quite a different mode of approach, resumed the studies begun in the 1920's by Carrel, Baker, and Ebeling, and began analyses by more modern methods of the serum, plasma, and embryo juice which constitute the classic Harrison-Burrows-Carrel nutrient. Morgan, Morton, and Parker have likewise undertaken the development of a defined nutrient and have, at the time of this writing, arrived at a formula which is somewhat similar to that of White (Morton, Morgan, and Parker, 1950).

Today all the basic techniques are under scrutiny and revision. Earle in particular has made a number of important contributions, such as substituting cellophane for the plasma substrate (Evans and Earle, 1947), altering the form of the Carrel flask to make manipulation easier and to permit quantitation of growth (Evans, Earle, Sanford, Shannon, and Waltz, 1951) by other than the classic planimetric method (see below), and devising means of sterilizing nutrients more satisfactorily than heretofore without loss of potency (Bryant, Earle, and Peppers, 1953).

Ever since the International Tissue Culture Conference, which was called in November, 1946, by the Committee on Growth of the National Research Council, the field has undergone a rejuvenation. It is being developed in many new directions by new workers, and bids fair to become in reality the important discipline which it potentially was from the beginning.

Ἀλλὰ δὲ ἐξ ὧν ταῦτα φλοιὸς ξύλον μήτρα, ὅσα ἔχει μήτραν. πάντα δ' ὁμοιομερῆ. καὶ τὰ τούτων δὲ ἔτι πρότερα καὶ ἐξ ὧν ταῦτα, ὑγρὸν ἴς φλὲψ σάρξ· ἀρχαὶ γὰρ αὗται· πλὴν εἴ τις λέγοι τὰς τῶν στοιχείων δυνάμεις, αὗται δὲ κοιναὶ πάντων. ἡ μὲν οὖν οὐσία καὶ ἡ ὅλη φύσις ἐν τούτοις.

❁   ❁   ❁

"AGAIN there are the things of which such parts (root, stem, leaf) are composed, namely, bark, wood, and core (in the case of those plants which have it), and these are all 'composed of like parts.' Further, there are the things which are even prior to these, from which they are derived—sap, fibre, veins, flesh; for these are elementary substances—unless one should prefer to call them the active principles of the elements; and they are common to all parts of the plant. Thus, the essence and entire material of plants consists in these."

THEOPHRASTUS. Enquiry into plants. I. II. I.
Translation by Sir Arthur Hort. Loeb Classical
Library (New York: G. P. Putnam's Sons, 1916).

Chapter 3

THE LIVING MATERIAL

A S WE have seen, the prime objective of most if not all cell culture work is the precise definition of those external and internal factors which control the formation, development, and behavior of the cells, tissues, and organs of which metazoa and metaphyta are constituted. For obvious reasons work with noncellular protozoa, protophyta, and bacteria which do not make up organic "societies" falls outside this terrain. The objective is approached by isolating the cell, tissue, organ, or organism from its fellows, *in vitro,* and following its development thus isolated. Any member which can be so isolated and grown is proper material for "tissue culture."

Choice of material will obviously be limited by a number of considerations. It must be *living* material—hair and fingernails of animals, or corky bark of trees will not be usable. It must not only be living, but it must be capable of growing, either as a primary function as in animal eggs or plant meristems, or by resumption of growth as in amphibian limb blastemas or plant-wound callus. Let us consider the materials in the two kingdoms which satisfy these requirements.

The fertilized egg, either of plant or animal, is in certain theoretical respects the ideal subject for cell culture. It is a single cell which we know possesses all the potentialities of all those cells which we find in the adult organism. The factors—all the factors—which determine the course of events by which those potentialities are evoked and segregated dur-

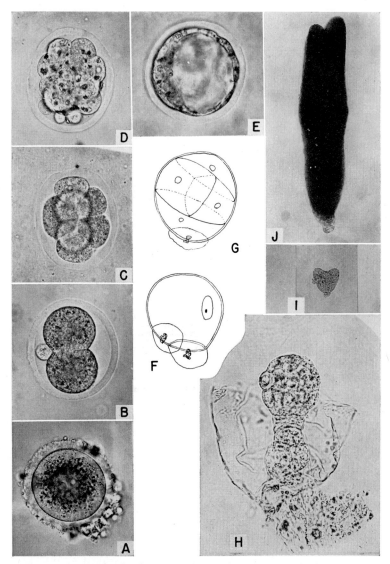

FIGURE 10. Early development of animal (mouse) and plant (banana and purslane) embryos. A, Single-celled mouse egg with its surrounding pellicle. B, Two-celled stage. C, Eight-celled stage. D, About 32 cells. E, Early blastula; the cells are now all oriented on the outside of a sphere, leaving the center filled with fluid. F, Single-celled egg of banana (*Musa*

ing development are of consequence to us. Extensive study of the embryology of such oviparous metazoa as worms, coelenterates, and amphibians bears witness to the interest of the subject. But oviparous embryology is not cell culture, and the eggs of viviparous organisms have proved unusually refractory objects for *in vitro* study. The physical conditions which surround the egg during its early development, protect it from untoward influences, and direct its unfolding, are extraordinarily complex. To date the egg cells of the viviparous metaphyta have not been successfully grown, and only a beginning has been made with those of the mouse, rabbit, monkey, and a few other metazoa (Chang, 1948, 1950; Chang and Pincus, 1951). These studies will have to wait on more refined techniques than are at present available, but they represent a very important challenge.

While the single-celled egg has proved refractory, the multicellular mass formed therefrom, the blastula of animals and the pro-embryo of plants, is much less so. Curtis has isolated the undifferentiated pro-embryo of orchids and has obtained from them unorganized cultures capable of apparently indefinite growth (Curtis and Nichol, 1948). The effect of certain barbiturates in suppressing the organization of such cultures is intriguing (Curtis, 1947). Blakeslee has made similar cultures from pro-embryos of *Datura* (van Overbeek, Conklin, and Blakeslee, 1941, 1942), Skoog from seedlings of *Pinus* (Loewenberg and Skoog, 1952), and Morel and Wetmore (1951; Wetmore and Morel, 1951a, b) from the gametophytes of certain ferns and mosses. In amphibians the cultures of cell groups isolated from the early

---

sapientum var. *seminifera*) showing the two degenerating synergids. G, Four-celled stage. H, Early embryo of purslane (*Portulaca oleracea*), a common weed; about 60 cells, with stalk. I, Heart-shaped embryo; this is about the earliest stage which has been successfully explanted and grown in culture. J, Young, but complete embryo (compare Figure 40). (A-E are from Lewis and Wright, 1935; F-G are redrawn from White, 1928; H-J are from White, 1932a)

blastula either by mechanical or chemical means (Holtfreter 1929, 1931) are likewise encouraging. The early explants of neural crest by Roux, Harrison, and others before the development of true "tissue cultures" should likewise fall in this category, as should Molliard's early attempts to cultivate parts of plant embryos. Certainly a great many important problems can be approached in this way. The cultivation of excised embryos *in vitro* as a means of overcoming certain types of hereditary sterility, as Tukey has done with stone fruits (1933, 1934), Blakeslee with *Datura,* Randolph with *Iris* (1945), and Nickell with *Malus* (1951), is an interesting offshoot. This approach has met with less success with animal embryos, but the same end result is brilliantly achieved by the transplantation of mammalian eggs into foster mothers, as in the case of mice (Runner, unpublished), rabbits (Chang, 1948, 1950), and cattle (Chang and Pincus, 1951).

When we pass beyond the pro-embryo stage, both plant and animal embryos take on sufficiently adult characteristics as to make it best to treat them as adults. Here we must deal with plants and animals separately.

Plants

From the time of germination until death, plants grow continuously, but they do not grow continuously in all their parts. An adult plant can be separated into perhaps four categories of cells. First there are the meristems, regions which are characteristically growing continuously, although seasonal factors may at times reduce their growth level to a minimum. These are the primary growing points—stem apices, root apices, lateral cambia, buds, and the intercalary meristems of grasses, some mints, lianas, and the like. Excised fragments containing any of these may be expected to grow actively, without any necessary lag period, if they are provided with a proper nutrient. Of these, the root apex, which can be excised by a single straight cut with a minimum of trauma, is the simplest. It served for the first successful plant tissue (organ) cultures (Robbins, 1922; Kotte, 1922; White, 1934a) and for most of the basic studies on tissue nutrition. Stem apices are equally suitable theoretically, but somewhat more difficult to divest of their enclosing wrappings (White, 1933a). The intercalary meristems of grasses, vines, and the great kelps, which can be excised with two straight cuts, should be almost as satisfactory but have not been extensively studied. The lateral cambia require for their excision the exposure of traumatized surfaces on all six faces of a cuboidal fragment but have proved to be excellent material in the hands of White (procambium of *Nicotiana,* 1939a), Gautheret *et al.* (cambia of *Ulmus,* Gautheret, 1940; *Vitis,* Morel, 1944b, 1945; *Rosa,* Nobécourt and Köfler, 1945, etc.), Gioelli (1938a, b), and others. The axillary gemmae of *Marattia* represent an example which has not, so far as I know, been investigated.

Closely related to these, but essentially distinct in character, is the group of secondary meristems—the phellogens, intercalated cambia, medullary ray parenchymas, the pericycle, etc.—which are capable of intermittent growth without preliminary dedifferentiation but do not normally grow with any continuity. The pericycle, which gives rise to lateral roots, is an excellent example. The lag period which intervenes between the excision of a bit of non-apical root tissue and the emergence of lateral roots therefrom (see below) is clear evidence of a resumption of a quiescent activity. The leaf-notch meristems of *Bryophyllum* are another example (Naylor, 1931). The carrot phloem cultures of Caplin and Steward (1949) fall into this category, as do many of the cultures originating in tuber tissues (Gautheret *et al.*). It should be noted that such potential meristems lie scattered through almost all living portions of plants and that as a consequence there are probably few parts of adult plants from which it should not, theoretically, be possible to isolate tissue cultures, difficult though this may prove to be in practice.

Beyond these, moreover, there is a very large group of tissues which, while already differentiated for other functions, are capable under suitable treatments of undergoing a dedifferentiation and acquiring meristematic potencies. The medullary and cortical parenchymas, certain types of epidermal cells, above all and most spectacularly the megaspore and microspore mother cells, tapetum and endosperm, and the lining of the ovarian wall which gives rise to apogamous embryos in the dandelion and grapefruit are examples of this category. So also are those pith tissues from which Gautheret has evoked growth by auxin treatment as in the case of the artichoke, and the potato tuber tissue investigated by Steward and Caplin (1951).

And finally there is a large group of cells which, while living and theoretically capable of growth, are nevertheless so highly differentiated and specialized either structurally or physiologically as to be refractory to any treatment. Stomatal guard cells, glandular hairs, trichomes, storage sclerenchymas such as that of the date seed, stone cells, wood tracheids, tannin cells, and the like, belong to this group. Interestingly enough, it was just this category of cells with which Haberlandt (1902) and his students wrestled unsuccessfully for nearly twenty years—sufficient reason for the three decades delay in achieving a successful culture!

Mention must be made here of certain cultures which do not fall easily into any of these groups since they are organ rather than tissue or cell cultures. These are the cultures

of flowers and fruits carried out by Nitsch (1949a, b, 1951),
of seed primordia by White (1932a), and the excised leaves
cultivated for special physiological purposes—for example,
the tobacco leaves grown by Dawson (1938; Vickery *et al.*,
1937) in studies of nicotine metabolism.

Animals

Unlike plants, in which there is no normal replacement of
deep-seated cells but in which there occurs a more or less
continuous marginal (terminal and lateral) growth and formation of new cells in specialized and local regions, in animals there is throughout life a constant destruction of worn-
out cells and their replacement throughout the body. This
is most rapid in young animals and in exposed regions such
as the skin or in very active organs such as the intestine.
But it occurs in almost all tissues. The muscles of the heart
and the neurones of the central nervous system appear to
be the only exceptions, and even these sometimes resume
replacement growth under special pathological conditions.

It should therefore be possible to grow as tissue cultures,
explants from any organ of the body at any age. The limitations are technical ones, not biological. Practice in fact
shows this to be true. Cultures of skin, epithelium of the
eye, kidney, liver, thyroid, ovary and other glands, bone,
nerve cells, connective tissue, skeletal muscle, tooth primordia, bone marrow, and white blood cells have all been
grown. Tissues taken from embryos in the early stages, of
which the chick embryo before the eighth day of incubation
may be taken as an example, will grow, that is, show active
migration and mitotic proliferation, without noticeable lag.
Tissues from older animals may be more sluggish.

Unfortunately there enters here a difficulty which is probably technical rather than biological. Under the classic

method of cultivation on a plasma-serum-embryo-juice sub-stratum (see below), there is a tendency for the "fibroblasts" or "histiocytes" to overrun and replace all other types of cells so that no matter what one starts with, if it is a mixed culture, he will end with a pure line of fibroblasts. It is possible to establish other types of cells only either by isolating pure lines from the beginning or by cultivating them on modified nutrients designed differentially to favor other than histio-cytic cells. The exact nature of the mechanism involved in the second method is still somewhat in doubt. Thus pure cultures of epithelium can be obtained from the margin of the iris, or of nerve cells from the spinal cord, by direct isolation.

Many authors have reported the transformation of histio-cytes, or of epithelial cells, into macrophages, and vice versa under the influence of special nutrients (Fischer, 1925, 1926; M. R. Lewis and W. H. Lewis, 1926). The latest is the report of Frederic (1951) of the derivation of macrophages from liver epithelium by the addition of choline in massive quan-tities ($M/100$ = ca. 0.12%!) to the nutrient (see also Chèvre-mont, 1943). In spite of their evidence it still appears uncertain if this is truly a reversible transformation of one cell type into another, or merely a nutritional segregation of a particular cell type from a mixture. The fact that it can be done only when starting from fresh embryonic tissue (Chèvremont) and fails if the cultures have first been "sta-bilized" by maintenance for several passages on the classic nutrient would certainly suggest segregation. The question will be definitely answered only when such transformations are observed in single-cell lines such as the "L" strain of Sanford, Earle, and Likely (1948).

Suffice it to say that any animal tissue, with the exception of heart muscle, liver parenchyma, and perhaps adult nerve can be "grown" in cell culture, and even these can be maintained for long periods and caused to migrate, alter their form, and extend their dimensions, though perhaps without formation of new muscle or nerve cells. Description of the exact methods of preparing particular tissues will be reserved for our chapter on the setting up of cultures.

"[My] ROOM was generally hung round with Guts, stomachs, bladders, preparations of parts and drawings. I had sand furnaces, Calots, Glasses and all sorts of Chymical Implements . . . Here I and my Associates often dined upon the same table as our dogs lay upon. I often prepared the pulvis fulminans and sometimes surprized the whole College with a sudden explosion. I cur'd a lad once of an ague with it, by fright. In my own Elaboratory I made large quantitys of sal volatile oleosum, Tinctura Metallorum, Elixir Proprietatis and such matters as would serve to put into our Drink."

> Diary of Mr. Wm. Stukeley, 1707, describing his rooms at Cambridge where he and his fellow student, Mr. Stephen Hales, planned and carried out some of the first real experiments in plant and animal physiology.
>
> (CLARK-KENNEDY, 1929)

Chapter 4

THE LABORATORY

THE GENERAL requirements for a cell culture laboratory are the same as those for any detailed microculture work: (1) facilities for the preparation, sterilization and storage of nutrients and for the cleansing of used equipment; (2) a place for the aseptic manipulation of tissue; (3) facilities for the maintenance of cultures under carefully controlled conditions; (4) facilities for examination and study of cultures in whatever way may be desired, and (5) a place for assembling and filing records. It will seldom be possible to carry on all these procedures in a single room with any degree of effectiveness, but the degree of complexity introduced into the organization of the laboratory will depend on the particular needs and the facilities available for any given work. The ideal organization would allow a separate room for each of the above functions—a media room, a transfer room, one or more culture rooms, a laboratory, and an office. All of these requirements will be essentially the same for either plant or animal studies.

The Media Room

The cleaning of glassware, preparation and sterilization of nutrients, and storage of supplies in readiness for use are services of the utmost importance for satisfactory cell culture work. The room in which these services are to be maintained, and its facilities, must therefore be given very careful consideration. The room need not be large nor elaborate but it must be adequate. The "media room" at the Mt. Desert Island Biological Laboratory, providing these services for a summer personnel of ten workers, is only 9 by 13 feet. This is too small to be fully satisfactory, but a room twice

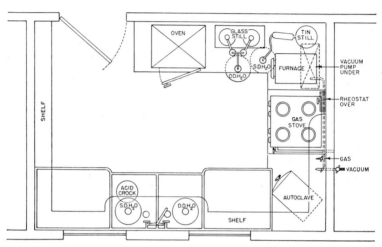

FIGURE 11. Ground plan of the preparation room in use at the Mt. Desert Island Biological Laboratory, Salisbury Cove, Maine. In a space of 9 by 12 feet this room includes all the important services required for cleaning and sterilizing equipment and supplies, and preparing nutrients for a laboratory of ten workers in the field of cell culture.

this size would be excellent. It is possible to include these facilities within a larger laboratory, but a separate room is to be preferred. Moreover it should, if at all possible, be reserved for cell culture work, since sharing it with bacteriologists, mycologists, and pathologists does involve the risk of contamination, both biological and chemical.

The room itself should have adequate light and ventilation. It must contain (1) a sink for washing glassware (see below) with adequate facilities for drainage, drying, and

storage; (2) a drying oven, preferably electric, for dry sterilization of glassware; (3) an autoclave for steam sterilization
of nutrients and of certain special equipment; (4) a muffle
furnace for baking filter candles; (5) one or more stills for
providing distilled water for the final cleansing of glassware
and for making up nutrients; (6) a good stove or hot plate

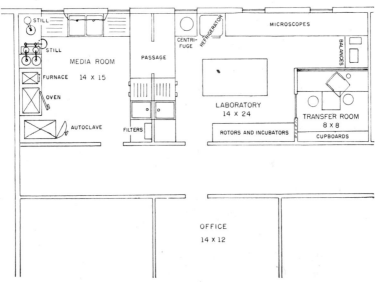

FIGURE 12. A suggested plan for preparation room, laboratory, transfer
room, and office for cell culture work.

for carrying on the many operations such as cleaning rubber
stoppers, filters, and the like, which require boiling; (7)
vacuum for filtrations and, if possible, compressed air for drying pipettes, etc.; and (8) tables of both standing and sitting
height at which such operations as wrapping glassware,
preparing cotton plugs, and the like can be carried out. A
chemical hood for handling fuming or otherwise dangerous
materials must be available but will be used so rarely that
it need not be housed in the cell culture department.

Washing Glassware

The washing of glassware is one of the most important and exacting procedures involved in cell culture work. For cultures on colloidal substrates such as agar, gelatin, or plasma, where the tissues are not in direct contact with the glass, routine washing with a detergent followed by simple rinsing may be sufficient to give satisfactory results, as it has in the Harvard laboratories where massive cultures of plant tissues are maintained on agar (Wetmore, personal communication). But where either plant or animal cells are grown in direct contact with the glass such methods are not likely to suffice. Experience has shown that for such cultures a much more thorough washing will be necessary; special attention must be paid to the facilities for this purpose.

Parker (1950), following the practice of Carrel, boils his glassware in white soap solution after which it is rinsed thoroughly with water, then rinsed with 95 per cent alcohol, and allowed to dry. It is then wrapped and dry sterilized. Vogelaar recommends washing in sodium pyrophosphate solution (1939). Cornman (1947) boils glassware in a meta-phosphate solution (Alkonox), rinses, boils with dilute HCl, rinses again, then rinses with 95 per cent alcohol and allows it to dry. Earle boils glassware in 80 per cent H_2SO_4 with a trace of HNO_3, then washes with water (1943a). This requires a hood and special "Duriron" kettles, which are very costly. Hanks (1952) uses an ingenious and thoroughly logical procedure which deserves further investigation. He starts from the premise that his cleaning procedure should contribute nothing which is not characteristic of the experimental environment of the cells. Soaps, strong acids, and alkalis are therefore not acceptable. But sodium-meta-silicate (water glass) satisfies this requirement. Hanks first rinses thoroughly with water or with a detergent; when protein residues are present, he subjects them to digestion with trypsin. He then places the glassware, mouths upward, in a series of enamel buckets, a separate container for each size and type of flask or tube, and each is covered with a stainless steel wire mesh cover, clamped on. The buckets are filled with a dilute solution of water glass (0.1 per cent in

FIGURE 13. Rinsing 16 by 150-mm. test tubes in dressing jars. A stainless steel screen cover held on with spring or screw clamps permits the jars to be inverted for rinsing and draining without the necessity of touching the tubes.

tap water). This is prepared as follows: Forty grams of calcium metaphosphate (Calgon) are dissolved in 3 liters of water, heating if necessary. Three hundred sixty grams of sodium metasilicate are suspended (they will not fully dissolve) in one liter of water. The two are then mixed, filtered, and used as a stock, which is diluted 1:100 for use. The glassware is boiled for 20 minutes in this solution. A hose is then inserted to the bottom of the bucket and the water glass washed out from the bottom so that the scum which sometimes forms on the fluid is washed away at the top and does not come in contact with the glass. The buckets are inverted to pour out the solution in the glassware, rinsed repeatedly but briefly with tap water, and allowed to drain thoroughly. Normal hydrochloric acid is added to neutralize the alkali residue, allowing 0.25 ml. per liter of container volume, and water is flowed in until the vessel is full. It is allowed to stand for 15 minutes, again decanted, rinsed twice with distilled water, and inverted to drain over night. The covers are then unclamped and the glassware is emptied out on a wire mesh. At no time is the glassware touched by the operator's hands before it is thoroughly dry, since even brief contact is presumed to contribute oily contaminations which would "creep" over the wet surface.

The result is certainly beautifully clean glassware. It is probable that what really happens is that a monomolecular layer of sodium silicate (glass!) is deposited on all exposed surfaces. The procedure, requiring as it does separate containers for the many different types of vessels used in a cell culture laboratory, is not simple. It is, however, highly effective and theoretically irreproachable, and might conceivably be simplified. It is certainly worth study.

In my own laboratory we have tried many methods of cleaning, and in spite of its many theoretically objectionable features, we have always returned to the use of a sulfuric acid potassium dichromate cleaning solution as being most satisfactory. We use a double stone sink with acid-proof Duriron traps and drains. On each side of this is built a wide drainage board covered with an acid-resistant lead sheet bent up to form a protective apron at the back and ends, down at the front, and over the edge of the sink. A 3- or 4-gallon vitreous crock with a cover is placed on wooden strips in the right-hand side of the sink, and a stainless steel tray 14 by 24 by 2 inches is propped up on a wooden strip on the right-hand drainage table, sloping toward the crock. The crock is filled to about 3 inches from the top with concentrated H_2SO_4 to which $K_2Cr_2O_7$ is added until an undissolved residue is left in the bottom. The glassware to be washed is first freed of all visible residue by brushing under tap water. It is then placed in the crock, being handled with acid-proof rubber gloves with gauntlets, care being taken that no air is occluded in the flasks. For small pieces of glassware it is desirable, though not essential, to have a 12-quart stainless steel pail with a number of holes bored in the bottom. This is placed in the crock, the small glassware being placed inside. The pail can be removed and drained as a whole without the necessity of handling each piece of glass separately. During the handling of glassware it is best to have a few inches of water in the sink to protect it from corrosion by undiluted acid if any is accidentally spilled.

Glassware is allowed to stand in the acid for a minimum of four hours. It is then removed with rubber gloves, superficially drained into the crock, and set up in the stainless steel tray for further draining. Subsequently the side of the sink containing the crock (usually the right-hand side) is filled with warm tap water and the glass is immersed therein piece by piece. Miscellaneous glassware is removed, rinsed in the opposite side of the sink in running tap water at least ten times, twice in single distilled water, once in double distilled water, and set aside to drain. Culture tubes can be assembled in stainless steel dressing jars, covered with a non-corrosive wire mesh cover as recommended by Hanks, filled, and emptied of water en masse.

This procedure is sufficient for routine glassware. For culture tubes, Carrel flasks, cover glasses, pipettes, etc., which come in direct contact with living tissues or with nutrients for long periods, we add as a final step a half-hour immersion in double distilled water in the autoclave. This will remove any traces of heavy metal ions which might have escaped the previous treatment.

While this procedure is certainly tedious, and the handling of large quantities of acid is hazardous, we believe that this method is nevertheless simpler in practice than those of Cornman, Earle, or Hanks, and more effective than those of Parker and of Vogelaar. The latter methods are certainly satisfactory for cultures maintained on plasma, agar, or other

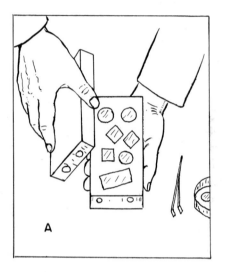

FIGURE 14. A, Method of drying cover glasses on a block covered with linen or silk over a loose pad of blotting paper. B, A wire rack for cover glasses made from ¼-inch mesh wire screen. (Compare with Fig. 19.)

organic substrates which are capable of separating the cultured cells from the glass by a detoxifying layer but are, we believe, not likely to prove completely satisfactory for cultures to be made in direct contact with glass, as in the cellophane technique (see below).

Pipettes are washed by a similar procedure but rinsed in an automatic pipette washer. Cover glasses are dropped one by one into a beaker of boiling metasilicate solution and simmered for 20 minutes with glass beads. They are rinsed for 5 minutes with a jet of water entering the container at the bottom and of sufficient force to "tumble" the glasses. The tap water is then replaced by distilled water, shaken, drained, and clean absolute alcohol is added. The cover glasses are finally removed singly with a cover-glass forceps, placed on a muslin-covered wood block, polished with a second similar covered block, and assembled in a small Petri dish for sterilization.

The actual arrangement of the sink will also require attention. We have found it best to place soiled glassware to the left of the sink itself, glassware in process of drainage, etc., to the right, and clean glassware on a 24 by 36-inch movable cart having a bottom shelf about 10 inches above floor level made of ½-inch mesh screen (hardware cloth), a removable second bottom about 24 inches off the floor made of 2-inch mesh screen (such as chicken wire), and two removable trays each 18 by 24 inches, one of hardware cloth, the other of chicken wire, arranged to set about 36 inches above floor level. These trays have 4-inch rims. Such items as large flasks can be placed mouth down through the chicken wire mesh to drain, smaller pieces resting on the smaller mesh tray. The bottom mesh will catch any pieces which may accidentally fall through the others. A broad shelf is suspended over the sink carrying two 20-liter Pyrex carboys, one for single distilled water, the other for double distilled water to be used for final rinsing. These are supplied with siphon outlets closed by pinch clamps. The openings are protected from actual contact with glassware and from lateral splash by glass "filling bells." No adequate precaution can be taken against direct vertical splash, but if the outlets are hung quite high, only a little below face level, they will be reasonably safe. It is not advisable to drain graduates over such a washing sink.

If distilled water is available as a laboratory supply, it should either be piped above the sink or 20-liter carboys should be placed above the sink. Water from any standard high-grade still will serve as "single distilled water." But for making up all nutrients, and for final rinsing and cleaning of all glassware, a second carboy of double distilled water should be provided. This should be redistilled from an all-Pyrex or quartz (Vicor) still. We have designed an all-Pyrex still with an automatic level control which has proved very satisfactory (White, 1953a). The distillate should be delivered directly into Pyrex containers and should at no time come in contact with metals or soft glass. All joints are ground, either standard taper or ball and socket type. Distilled water prepared and stored in this way is adequate for most purposes. It should be remembered, however, that water stored in Pyrex cannot be used for studies involving questions of boron deficiency, since Pyrex is a borosilicate of a solubility sufficient to provide the boron required by plant tissues, and that any contact with rubber, even the purest available, may vitiate experiments on sulfur or zinc requirements. For these purposes special sources of distilled water may have to be provided.

Sterilizing Equipment

Second in importance only to the dish-washing equipment and that for preparing distilled water is the equipment for sterilization of nutrients and supplies. The general theory and practice of sterilization is treated thoroughly in Underwood's textbook of sterilization (1941), and in Parker's text (1950). Equipment for the purpose will consist of three items, intended respectively for "dry" sterilization of glassware (flasks, tubes, pipettes, filters, etc.); for "wet" sterilization of heat-stabile solutions (items of equipment like rubber, cellophane, or other partly heat-labile materials, must be included, such as filter columns, stoppers, rubber

FIGURE 15. A, Glass still used in redistilling water for cell culture work. The still has an automatic level control which permits it to be operated with a minimum of attention (see White, 1953a). B, Electric oven of a type found particularly satisfactory for dry sterilization of pipettes, Petri dishes, slides, etc. (Courtesy of Wm. Boekel Co., Philadelphia)

gloves, etc.; and for filtration of solutions which are heat-labile to such an extent that they cannot be autoclaved, as is the case with protein materials, some vitamins, carbonate solutions, and the like.

The drying oven should be large enough to provide adequate space for all exigencies. An electric oven is to be preferred. We have found the Boekel 31 by 31 by 21-inch type highly satisfactory. While a temperature of 160°C. is generally recommended, we have found that if glassware wrapped in muslin, paper, or foil is so arranged as to allow reasonably free penetration of heat and is left for at least 4 hours at a temperature of 140°C. (timing should begin only *after* this temperature has been reached), sterilization will be quite adequate and will result in less charring of cotton or paper where these cannot be dispensed with. Charring is to be avoided since distillation of cellulose products, unless highly purified, may result in the formation of tars which are extremely toxic to living cells. Charred cotton also falls into pieces which may seriously obscure cultures and possibly affect them nutritionally. We avoid the use of paper and cotton wherever possible and use aluminum foil for most wrapping. Cotton plugs, where it is necessary to use them for tubes and flasks, are made of non-absorbent cotton covered with fine bandage muslin. This prevents fibers from pulling loose and either sticking to the glass or falling into solutions. They are either sterilized in their flasks or tubes, or placed in glass or stainless steel jars. In any case they should be autoclaved rather than dry sterilized. Cotton must also be used to plug pipettes and filter columns (see below).

To prevent breakage, we place a wad of glass wool wrapped in glass cloth in the bottom of pipette cans. Standard (100 mm.) Petri dishes are dry sterilized in regular Petri-dish cans sold for this purpose or they can be wrapped in paper, muslin, or foil in groups of three or four. The smaller ones (60 mm.) can be stacked in suitable cans such as the 70 by 100-mm. cans used for fruit juices, capped with aluminum foil. (Do not use cans lined with plastic!) Balloon flasks and others requiring dry sterilization will likewise be capped with foil.

Standard pipettes are placed in metal cans. Inoculating pipettes are usually sterilized in large test tubes, although Gey and Cameron (see Cameron, 1950, Fig. 4) have special

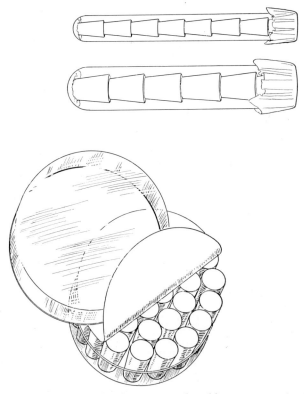

FIGURE 16. Two methods of storing sterile rubber stoppers. At the top, a 16 by 150-mm. test tube with seven No. 00 stoppers (for Carrel flasks) and a 25 by 150-mm. tube with five No. 0 stoppers (for roller tubes). At the bottom, a Petri dish with 50 No. 00, 30 No. 0, or 7 No. 4 stoppers.

glass containers for this purpose. Culture tubes are first autoclaved, mouth up, in double distilled water, in stainless steel dressing jars, and are then dry sterilized in the same cans after draining off the water. Instruments may be sterilized in the oven or autoclave, or by boiling in water, or they may be dipped in alcohol, or flamed. For most purposes, we prefer boiling.

Like the oven, the autoclave must be adequate in size. A 22 by 40-inch size is excellent for routine large-scale work. It may be placed in the media room, or, if it is to be shared with other departments (bacteriology, microbiology, medical technology, etc.) as is often necessary, it may be placed elsewhere in the building. If the latter is the case it may be usefully supplemented by a smaller autoclave in the media room, since there will be many routine sterilizing operations of small volume but requiring immediate attention. The larger autoclave should be of the double-jacket type, which permits vacuum drying of stoppers and the like, as well as the usual steam sterilization.

Rubber stoppers can be placed in Petri dishes, small end down, or in suitable test tubes. In Petri dishes, a sheet of hard (qualitative) filter paper should be placed between the stoppers and glass to prevent sticking. A 100-mm. Petri dish will hold about 50 No. 00, 30 No. 0, or 7 No. 4 stoppers. The dishes should be wrapped in paper, muslin, or foil. If test tubes are used, a disk of glass cloth in the bottom of the tube will prevent the stoppers from sticking.

Operating Rooms

It is absolutely necessary that tissues under operation, the implements, culture vessels, etc., shall be protected from all possible contamination from outside sources. The classic method of attaining this end is by the provision of a special transfer room, the wearing of surgical gowns and masks, the use of disinfecting sprays, baths, swabs, etc., the provision of large numbers of interchangeable implements, the maintenance of complete silence in the culture room, and similar expedients. While it is nice to have stainless steel operating rooms, skylights, gray finish walls, steam jets, etc., and to wear black gowns and masks if one is so inclined, none of these things is necessary, and some are actually to be avoided. We will proceed, therefore, from the complex to the simple.

An ideal operating and transfer room will be an inside room, about 8 by 10 feet with an 8-foot ceiling. The walls should be of smooth finish—steel, Carrara-glass, tile, enamel paint, or simply waxed asbestos board (transite)—and should be as free as possible of fixtures which might catch dust. A dark gray color is best, but light gray or green is also good; white is likely to give poor contrast and to be distracting. There should be no heating unit of the usual type in the room, since radiators are constant sources of dirt, convection currents, and the like. Heating and ventilation should be provided by an air-conditioning unit. A small unit consisting of fan and filters, such as those sold to hay-fever sufferers for installation in or below a window, is ideal for the purpose.[1] This should be installed above the door, forcing into the room filtered air already warmed to room temperature. The door itself should have a glass and should either swing out or slide. If filtered air is blown into the room under positive pressure and escapes through and around the door, there will be little danger of contaminating dust getting in, even when the door is opened. Light is best provided by a skylight, but well placed windows and recessed artificial lighting fixtures will satisfy the need. The only stipulation is that all windows should be absolutely airtight; if outside windows are used, they should be double. This is to reduce the temperature drop and consequent convection currents which a cold glass will create, and is one reason for preferring an inside room without windows.

The room should be provided with electricity, and if possible, water, vacuum, and compressed air. I prefer that it

[1] The "Airking B" sold by the Berns Manufacturing Co., Chicago, is particularly satisfactory for this purpose.

should not be provided with gas fixtures, as gas is highly toxic to many tissues, but a plastic (Tygon or Silicone) line can be run in from an outside jet through a small hole in the wall if so desired, or a flame can be furnished from a good alcohol lamp. A table-height shelf 30 inches wide should be built along one side of the room. This should be hung from brackets and should not have legs running to the floor, since these are always a source of accumulated dirt. There should also be a small movable table, about 2 by 2 feet, which, when set against the side shelf, provides a T-shaped unit where two operators can face one another across the movable table while the fixed shelf provides a place for added equipment within easy reach. Table tops should be of black "Formica," wood, or slate. They should never be made of stainless steel, which gives a reflecting surface against which it is impossible to see well and a surface so smooth that the least moisture causes glass objects to "stick" to an objectionable degree. The floor should be linoleum, tile, or some other easily cleaned surface.

Such a room provides an aseptic atmosphere, and permits free movement and manipulation. Nevertheless, the operator will bring some contaminations in with him unless he wears the classic sterile surgeon's gown, hood, and mask, and unless he reduces movement and conversation to a minimum. These are annoying restrictions. We have obviated them by placing on the table one or the other of two types of shield. The simpler is a piece of plate glass 20 inches square, held in a frame 9 inches above the table, the frame being so built that the front and most of the two sides and back are open. With this on the table so placed that the front edge of the glass projects an inch or so beyond the edge of the table, dissections and manipulations can be made freely under the glass, protected completely from falling dust, from the breath of the operators, and from anything except fairly violent air currents. Gowns, hoods, and masks are unneces-

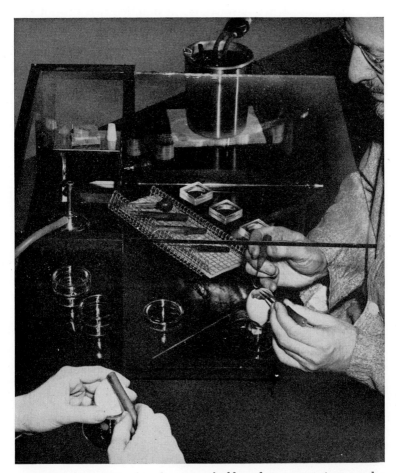

FIGURE 17. A plate glass dissecting shield used to protect tissues under manipulation from contamination by dust. Here chick embryos are being removed from the eggs for the preparation of cultures. This picture also shows the use of a beaker and immersion heater for sterilizing instruments, a wire rack for instruments, the use of paired Columbia watch glasses as recipients for tissues and organs during the stages of dissection and washing, and the "button-hook" with which chick embryos are removed from the egg. (Compare with Fig. 19.)

sary and, in fact, we have found in practice that all but the most prolonged operations can be carried out under a shield in a regular laboratory room without resort to a special transfer room. Similar protection is provided in a somewhat less adaptable but highly effective form by the double-glass table tops (one glass about 8 inches above the other) installed in

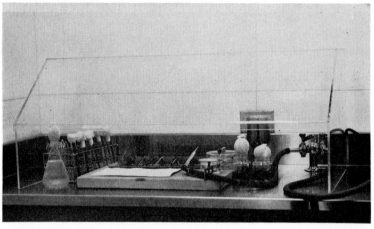

FIGURE 18. A somewhat larger hood of "Lucite," employed in performing operations such as the weighing of cultures which require prolonged exposure. (Designed by and built for the author. Photograph by courtesy of Dr. Theodore S. Hauschka.)

the laboratories of the Department of Surgical Pathology at Columbia University College of Physicians and Surgeons.

A somewhat more elaborate hood which serves the same purpose and has proved especially valuable in making aseptic weighings, and mass transfers such as those used in dealing with plant cultures, etc., is made of transparent plastic (Lucite). It is 38 inches wide, 24 inches deep, and 12 inches high. The front is open to a height of 6 inches, above which the face slopes back at a 45° angle, leaving a flat top 12 inches wide. Back, ends, and top are closed, the bottom and front being open. This provides complete protection from dust and from air currents, while permitting free manipulation and complete visibility. We have set a precision torsion balance inside such a hood, with an alcohol lamp or micro-burner alongside for flaming tubes, and have made hundreds of weighings of cultures with a minimum of contamination. This is entirely adequate for most purposes without a transfer room. Further details on the use of the transfer room will be presented in a later chapter dealing with the actual setting up of cultures.

Implements and Glassware

The variety of paraphernalia which has been used in making tissue cultures in one laboratory or another is legion and if brought together in one place might well frighten the uninitiated. However, it will seldom happen that a single laboratory will carry on all types of cultures or make extensive use of all techniques. The equipment actually needed in any one laboratory is not great.

Every laboratory must of course have a basic supply of graduates, bottles, filters, and the like. We use Pyrex serum bottles of 4-, 9-, and 20-liter capacity in making up, sterilizing, and storing large volumes of solutions. Our stock solutions of salts for plant cultures, for example, are stored in 4-liter or 9-liter serum bottles painted black to exclude light. In making up solutions in quantities of not more than one liter we prefer balloon flasks rather than Erlenmeyers, since they can be rinsed out more effectively and can be heated more safely over the flame, if required. We therefore keep a supply of short-necked Pyrex balloon flasks of 125-, 200-, 500- and 1,000-ml. capacity, with cork rings to set them on. The only special item used in making up nutrients is the Mudd filter column which we find superior to any other equipment for the sterile collection of filtered fluids. The columns need not, however, be graduated. For sterile filtra-

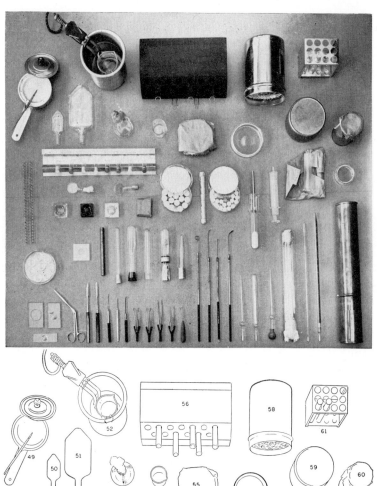

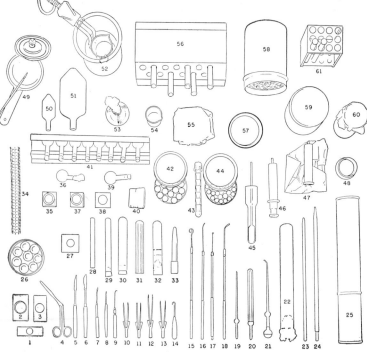

FIGURE 19. Assembled equipment for preparing cultures of both plant and animal material in hanging drops, flasks, and tubes. (*Explanation on page 63*)

1. Small hollow-ground slide for hanging drop cultures.
2. Large optically flat hollow-ground slide for phase contrast and cinematographic study.
3. Large hollow-ground slide for Maximow double cover-slip cultures.
4. Heyman ear-and-throat scissor used in cutting cultured root tips in 125-ml. Erlenmeyer flasks.
5. Pointed scalpel for dissecting plant materials.
6. Round-bladed scalpel used in cutting up animal tissues.
7. Knife made by spot-welding a chip of razor blade to a needle, for fine dissections.
8. Cataract knife for fine dissections.
9. A right-angle needle-knife used for fine dissections such as those on chick embryos.
10. Curved mosquito forceps.
11. Straight mosquito forceps.
12. Curved medium forceps.
13. Straight medium forceps.
14. A "button-hook" for lifting out chick embryos.
15. Spiral transfer loop suitable for handling large plant callus cultures.
16. A fine curved spatula used for handling small plant cultures and for scraping Carrel flasks carrying pure-strain cultures of animal cells.
17. Small loop for transferring root cultures.
18. Spatula used to remove plasma clot from Carrel flasks, for subculturing.
19. Pipette with blown bulb for handling small quantities of fluid nutrients and for inoculating Carrel flasks.
20. A similar pipette in its protective 16 by 150-mm. tube.
21. Pipette of the curved Gey type used in inoculating roller tubes.
22. A large test tube serving as a container for inoculating pipettes.
23. One-ml. pipette for transferring nutrients.
24. Ten-ml. pipette for transferring nutrients.
25. Copper pipette can.
26. Petri dish containing eight small U. S. Bureau of Plant Industry type Syracuse watch glasses suitable for cultures of small plant or animal parts.
27. Maximow type watch glass with optically flat bottom.
28. Steel rod used to crack egg shells.

29. Test tube, 16 by 150 mm., for animal or plant roller-tube cultures.
30. Test tube, 25 by 150 mm., with agar and plugged with cotton as is the case when sterilizing for use with plant callus cultures.
31. A 25 by 150-mm. tube, empty.
32. A similar tube, now capped with aluminum foil, which replaces the cotton plug.
33. A 15-ml. conical centrifuge tube for embryo extract, covered with a stamped aluminum cap.
34. Wire rack for holding clean cover slips.
35. Embryological watch glass, clear.
36. Carrel flask with cotton plug.
37. Embryological watch glass, black.
38. Two Columbia watch glasses used for washing small animal organs.
39. Carrel flask with perforated cellophane insert and rubber stopper.
40. Two Columbia watch glasses wrapped for sterilization.
41. Metal rack for Carrel flasks.
42. Petri dish with sterile No. 0 stoppers.
43. Test tube with sterile No. 00 stoppers.
44. Petri dish with sterile No. 00 stoppers.
45. TenBroeck-Potter type tissue grinder for preparing embryo extract.
46. A 20-ml. syringe used for preparing embryo extract (alternate).
47. A 20-ml. syringe partly wrapped for sterilization.
48. A 60-mm. Petri dish used to handle chick embryos and in which to wash plant roots, etc.
49. "Egg poacher" used to hold hot paraffin-vaseline mixture for sealing on cover slips for hanging-drop cultures.
50. Small hexagonal culture flask (Earle).
51. Large hexagonal culture flask (Earle).
52. Stainless steel beaker and immersion heater used for sterilizing instruments.
53. Erlenmeyer flask, 125 ml., used for plant root and callus cultures.
54. A 50-ml. beaker.
55. Petri dishes with stoppers, wrapped for sterilizing.
56. Wooden block for test tubes.
57. Petri dish, 100 mm.
58. Stainless steel dressing jar with sterile culture tubes.
59. Metal Petri dish can.
60. Can containing 60-mm. Petri dishes.
61. Metal rack for test tubes.

tion the sintered glass filters manufactured by Corning are effective and rapid, and being all glass, are irreproachable from the biological point of view. They are, however, expensive and rather fragile, and have the added disadvantage of not permitting high temperature cleaning. We therefore prefer to use the small (15 by 55 mm.) Selas porcelain filters. These are effective, very uniform, rugged, and can be freed of organic residues by baking at 600°C. followed by simple rinsing with water. Larger sizes may also be used but are seldom needed in routine work. Their only defects are (1) the presence of a rubber stopper between filter, Pyrex protecting cylinder, and filter column, and (2) the fact that at best the last 3 or 4 ml. of fluid cannot be recovered from them. Both these defects can be obviated by placing the filter inside the filter column or flask and feeding the material to be filtered into the inside of the filter with a pipette or through a thistle tube, but this of course reduces the effective filtering area. Their detailed manipulation will be discussed later. We use pipettes of 10-ml. and 5-ml. capacity graduated to 0.1 ml. and 2 ml., and 1 ml. graduated to 0.01 ml. We also use special inoculating pipettes, which will be considered later. These are all plugged with cotton and sterilized in standard brass pipette cans or large test tubes. Beyond these items all the glassware used in preparing nutrients is standard and found in every well equipped microbiological laboratory.

Special Glassware

Culture Vessels.—Culture vessels consist of various types of (1) slides, (2) flasks, (3) tubes, and (4) watch glasses.

Slides.—Ordinary 1 by 3- and 2 by 3-inch slides are standard and are used for many purposes. In addition hollow-ground slides of the deep Rockefeller Institute type will sometimes be used. The shallow-ground slides of the type used by protozoologists are valueless for tissue cultures. Pierced slides of both 1- and 2-inch width, either of glass, plastic, or aluminum, and of both 2-mm. and 5-mm. thickness will be needed for "sitting drop" cultures (see below).

Flasks.—For root cultures and for growing relatively large masses of plant tumor and cambial tissues on agar, standard 125-ml. Erlenmeyer flasks are often used. Riker uses for the latter purpose a 6-ounce flat medicine bottle ("Blake bottle") (Riker and Gutsche, 1948). This last somewhat resembles Earle's "modified whiskey bottle," which is coming into extensive use for the maintenance of stocks of animal cells grown under cellophane. Brues has also used a small flat medicine bottle with one side bored out and covered with a cemented-on No. 2 cover glass for close study of animal tissues (Shaw, Kingsland, and Brues, 1940). Besides these, the only flasks in common use are the D-3.5 Carrel flask and the Porter "roller flask" (Porter, Claude, and Fullam, 1945; Porter, 1947). These are excellent for the prolonged study of animal cells under the high power of the microscope. Both the Carrel flask and the Porter flask are clumsy and expensive, however, and are to be avoided where possible.

Tubes.—For most plant tissue cultures other than roots and embryos, a 25 by 150-mm. Pyrex test tube has proved most satisfactory. Gautheret and his group use these tubes in a vertical position with a single culture per tube. White slopes the tubes sharply, exposing a greater area of agar; this permits growing two or three cultures in each tube. Sloped tubes are also easier to inoculate.

The 25 by 150-mm. tube is too large for satisfactory animal tissue cultures. But the standard 16 by 150-mm. tube used in bacteriological work has proved extremely valuable for the roller-tube method, which has largely replaced the Carrel flask for routine cultures. These tubes are sterilized (see above) and stored in either stainless steel or "tin" cans.

Waymouth (1950) has designed a large-diameter hexagonal tube, similar to but larger than that projected by Gey (1936), which is especially satisfactory for the incubation and serial removal of six narrow insert cover slips, one attached to each face of the tube, on which cultures can be grown for subsequent staining and the preparation of permanent slides.

Closure.—For plant cultures, free circulation of air is important. The vessels have therefore usually been closed with cotton plugs wrapped in muslin. These have the disadvantage of allowing rather too rapid evaporation of the culture fluid, of permitting the entry of mites, and in damp weather of mold hyphae, and of being rather messy in general. For short-term cultures of not more than a week or so duration the vessels may be closed with rubber stoppers, but this reduces the air supply too drastically to be tolerated if the tubes are to remain closed for more than ten days. For most routine experiments we have found a simple closure with aluminum foil, without plug, highly satisfactory (see below).

Unlike plant cultures, animal cultures require that the closure be airtight (rubber stoppers), since any gas exchange permits the escape of CO_2 and a resultant unacceptable rise in pH. For this reason animal cultures must also have their air supply renewed at frequent intervals. Rubber stoppers, either natural or synthetic, contain diffusible toxic substances which may become a hazard if fluids condense on them. If there is any chance of fluids coming in contact with the stoppers, either directly or by condensation, it is preferable to use the white West "formula 124" stopper.[2] This is relatively non-toxic. It is available in two sizes, S-43 suitable for Carrel flasks (No. 00), and S-41, corresponding to the No. 0 stoppers suitable for 16-mm. tubes. The West Company also makes a more expensive pure silicone stopper.

[2] The West Co., Phoenixville, Pa.

Watch Glasses.—For dissections, the so-called "Columbia embryological watch glass" has proved most satisfactory. These are placed face to face in pairs, separated by a sheet of hard chemically inert paper, so that one glass serves as a cover for the other, wrapped with foil, and autoclaved. This type has not been used as a culture dish, although it might prove useful for any purpose for which the deep hollow-ground slides are employed. Fell uses for the cultivation of embryonic femurs, and the like, a standard chemical watch glass of about the same size (5 cm.), placed in a larger Petri dish with an inlay of moist cotton to maintain humidity (Fell, 1928a, b; see also Pomerat, 1951). Gaillard (1948) uses standard embryological watch glasses with plasma for the cultivation of excised ovaries, covering the dishes with standard square covers. In my laboratory we have used the United States Department of Agriculture small-type (27-mm. outside, 20-mm. cavity) Syracuse watch glass, eight glasses per Petri dish, covered with 25-mm. round cover glasses. These are ideal for the cultivation of various types of plant embryos, algal sporelings (Davidson, 1950), Entomostraca, and the like. They should be equally effective for animal organ cultures.

Miscellaneous.—In addition to the items listed above, a few hypodermics will be needed. Those of 1-ml. capacity with No. 22 needles ¾ inch long will be used in measuring small amounts of such trace nutrients as insulin, thyroxin, vitamin C, etc. They are also used in many laboratories for dispensing serum, plasma, and nutrients to hanging-drop cultures, where very small volumes are required. Those of 20-ml. capacity, without needle, will be used for trituration of embryos, the embryos being forced through the syringe into a 15-ml. conical centrifuge tube. Those of 30-ml. capacity with No. 18 needles 2 inches long will be used for drawing blood from the hearts of cockerels or rabbits.

Inoculating pipettes are of three types. The type used in many laboratories is the so-called "Pasteur pipette." It consists of a piece of 4-mm. hard glass tubing drawn out to a long point one mm. in diameter and bent at right angles for the terminal 5 mm. The tip is sealed as it is drawn out so that the interior is sterile. This tip is broken off immediately before use, the tissue or nutrient is manipulated with a haemocytometer mouth tube, and the entire pipette is discarded after use. This is obviously wasteful of glass and in our experience is unnecessary. The type of pipette used by Gey is equally effective and seems to us more sensible. A piece of 6-mm. tubing is cut to about 20 cm. in length. It is heated in the center and drawn out to provide a central segment about 2 mm. in diameter and 20 cm. long, and is then cut in two. The drawn-out tips are lightly fire-polished and then bent at about a 60° angle for a length of about 7–8 mm. These pipettes are plugged with cotton and sterilized in large test tubes or in special glass containers. They can be manipulated either with a mouth tube or with standard Becton and Dickenson red rubber bulbs and can be cleaned and used repeatedly. They are very satisfactory, especially in working with roller-tube cultures.

In my own laboratory we use a special pipette which has certain advantages. The tip is essentially identical with the Gey type. The shaft is shorter, about 20 cm. over-all length. The upper end is provided with a bulb about 3 cm. from the end, and above this is a constriction to prevent the cotton plug from being forced into the bulb. The bulb permits manipulation of fairly large quantities of fluid without danger of wetting the cotton plug and without the need for the greater length of the Gey type. The bulb is also of such a diameter and such a distance from the tip that a single pipette will rest in a 16 by 150-mm. test tube with the tip about half a centimeter from the bottom. Pipettes in such tubes are sterilized in a can or jar. The pipette and its tube can be handled without exposing the tip, can be examined and a suitable tip selected, and can be returned to the tube without danger of contamination. While fairly expensive (about $1.25 apiece), the evident advantages would seem to justify the cost.

This covers the equipment and space which is necessary for setting up tissue cultures. Some of the equipment will be discussed in more detail later. It is unnecessary to outline in detail the equipment and space for laboratories, storage rooms, and offices, as these will differ with each type of problem and with each organization.

"ROUND about the cauldron go;
In the poison'd entrails throw.
Toad,[1] that under a cold stone
Days and nights has thirty-one
Swelter'd venom sleeping got,
Boil thou first i the charmed pot.[2]
Fillet of a fenny snake,
In the cauldron boil and bake,
Eye of newt and toe of frog,
Wool of bat and tongue of dog,[3]
Adder's fork and blind-worm's
    sting,
Lizard's leg and howlet's wing,[4]
Scale of dragon, tooth of wolf,
Witches' mummy; maw and gulf,
Of the ravin'd salt [5] sea shark,
Root of hemlock digg'd i the dark,
Liver [6] of blaspheming Jew,
Gall of goat, and slips of yew
Sliver'd in the moon's eclipse,
Nose of Turk and Tartar's lips,
Finger of birth-strangled babe [7]
Ditch-deliver'd by a drab,
Make the gruel thick and slab:
Add thereto a tiger's chaudron,
For the ingredients of our
    cauldron,
Cool it with a baboon's blood,[8]
Then the charm is firm and
    good!"

SHAKESPEARE, *Macbeth*, Act IV, Scene I.

[1] Harrison (1907) started tissue culture with "lymph of frog."

[2] One sees such pots in Earle's wash room (Earle, 1943a).

[3] While Doljanski (Doljanski and Hoffman, 1943) recommended adult tissue, the usual practice has been to employ embryo juices. Chick embryo is most commonly used (Carrel, 1913b) but beef (Gey and Gey, 1936) or dog serves equally well.

[4] Chicken wing blood is also often used (see Cameron, 1950).

[5] Doubtless the salts of Tyrode solution (1910).

[6] Liver extract has been used by Baker and Carrel (1928) as a substitute for embryo-juice.

[7] Many laboratories still use human placental cord serum. It can be purchased from Difco (*Difco Manual*, 9th Ed., 1953) and from Microbiological Associates.

[8] A fibrin clot serves equally well (Porter 1947), as does chick plasma (Burrows, 1910a).

Chapter 5

NUTRIENTS

THE ORIGINAL tissue culture nutrient of Harrison consisted simply of a drop of clotted lymph from the frog (1907). Burrows early substituted a clot prepared from chicken plasma (1910a, b). This was both mechanical support and nutrient, and was excellent for short-term cultures but would not support unlimited and rapid growth. Carrel greatly improved the nutritive conditions by adding an extract of chick embryos (1913b). From these basic ingredients have been developed most of the present-day complex media for animal cultures, including fibrin-thrombin clots (Porter, 1947), tissue extracts (Carrel, 1913b; Doljanski and Hoffman, 1943; M. R. Lewis and W. H. Lewis, 1911b), and others. The cellophane substratum of Evans and Earle (1947), and the so-called "synthetic nutrient" of Baker (1936), of Baker and Ebeling (1939), and of Fischer *et al.* (1941a, b, *et seq.*) are outgrowths of this approach.

At about the same time that Carrel was developing the use of embryo juice the two Lewises (1911a, b, *et seq.*) began a study of the effects of particular ingredients, especially the inorganic salts, on the growth of animal tissue cultures. Out of this approach has come the salt solutions of Gey (1936) and others, and by projection the synthetic nutrients of White (1946, 1949) and of Morgan, Morton, and Parker (1950).

The tissue extract approach, as we have already seen, did not prove workable in dealing with plant tissues. For them synthetic nutrients were from the start the only ones which proved effective. The development of satisfactory nutrients for plant tissues had to await the accumulation of an adequate knowledge of nitrogenous and vitamin nutrition. As a result plant nutrients, while historically late-comers, are nevertheless simpler and more precisely defined than those for animal tissues, and will be dealt with first.

A nutrient for any tissue, plant or animal, must supply all the essential materials available *in vivo* in the tissue juices. In plants these "juices" are two, conveyed in and diffusing from the xylem on the one hand and the phloem on the other. The xylem "sap" moves upward in the plant from the soil toward the leaves, in the so-called "transpiration stream." Its major constituents, quantitatively at least, are the inorganic salts and although there is some differential absorption or exclusion of particular ions, this is in most important respects equivalent to a "good" soil solution. Based on this fact a series of excellent nutrient solutions for plant cultures (not plant tissue cultures) were developed more than a century ago, beginning with the work of Woodward (1699) and Duhamel (1765). That of Knop (1865) has been used by Gautheret (1935), and of Pfeffer [1] by Robbins (1922a, b) as inorganic bases for tissue culture nutrients. White (1932b, 1933b) used as a base the solution of Uspenski and Uspenskaia (1925) because of its greater stability over a wide pH range. Trelease and Trelease have developed a complex salt solution for the same reason (1933). The most complete solution is probably that of Hoagland and Snyder (1933). In practice all of these are effective.

The second "sap," that which is carried in the phloem, moves characteristically downward from the leaves to the

[1] The solution commonly known as "Pfeffer's solution" and given on p. 113 of Pfeffer's *Pflanzenphysiologie* (2d ed.; Leipzig: Engelmann) appears to be merely Pfeffer's formula for the improved solution given by Knop (1884, *Versuchsstat.* **30:** 292–94) and is in no way original with Pfeffer.

roots and contains materials synthesized in the photosynthetic tissues of the plant. It is characterized by a low inorganic and high organic content. Its chief constituents (again quantitatively) are sucrose (or dextrose) and asparagine (Borodin, 1878; Murneek, 1935) or glutamine (Vickery, Pucher, and Clark, 1936; Archibald, 1945). Attempts to establish nutrients for plant tissue cultures by adding asparagine and dextrose to a Knop salt solution, as Kotte did (1922), were not successful and many years of research intervened before it was discovered that although carbohydrate and amino acid were the ingredients of phloem sap most in evidence quantitatively, there did exist certain things called "vitamins" which, although not so evident, were of equal importance.

This discovery was indirect. Kotte (1922) had found a digest of Liebig's meat extract a partially effective supplement for a Knop-dextrose-asparagine nutrient. Robbins (1922b) had used a yeast autolyzate with equal but still only partial success. White showed that by substituting sucrose for dextrose (1934a, 1940a, b) and utilizing a nonautolyzed yeast extract, a fully adequate nutrient could be provided (1934a). He then analyzed the yeast (1937a) and showed that its effects were due to its content of amino acids (1937b), especially glycine (1939c) on the one hand and of vitamins, especially thiamine, on the other (White, 1937c; see also Robbins and Bartley, 1937). Robbins and Schmidt (1938, 1939a, b, c) then added pyridoxin and nicotinic acid to the list of beneficial though "non-essential" substances (in the sense of being synthesized in minimal but suboptimal quantities by the tissue itself). Morel (1946) and others have since added biotin and pantothenate as essential for certain tissues (Gautheret, 1950). At present there are a great many nutrient formulas for plant tissues available. Of these, the most widely used are modifications of those of White and of Gautheret.

White's solution (1943a, b) consists of three parts: an inorganic salt solution, a carbohydrate, and a vitamin supplement. These are prepared as follows. Using the best grades of analytical chemicals, the following are weighed out:

$Ca(NO_3)_2$	20 g.	$MnSO_4$	0.45 g.
Na_2SO_4	20 g.	$ZnSO_4$	0.15 g.
KCl	8 g.	H_3BO_3	0.15 g.
NaH_2PO_4	1.65 g.	KI	0.075 g.

These are dissolved one at a time in 8 liters of double distilled water. If hydrates of any salts are used, be sure to make the proper corrections in weights! Thirty-six grams of $MgSO_4$ are dissolved separately in 2 liters of water. The two are then mixed slowly in a 10-liter serum bottle. This stock is ten times the concentration needed in the complete nutrient. It should be stored in a black bottle or in the dark. As a second stock dissolve 300 mg. glycine, 50 mg. nicotinic acid, 10 mg. thiamine, and 10 mg. pyridoxine in 100 ml. of water. This is distributed in 10-ml. aliquots in test tubes, stoppered, and stored in the refrigerator. This stock is 100 times the concentration used.

Two liters make a convenient amount of nutrient. Dissolve 40 g. of C.P. sucrose in one liter of water. Dissolve 10 mg. $Fe_2(SO_4)_3$ in 100 ml. of water, discard half [2] and add the remainder to the sugar solution. To these, 200 ml. of stock salt solution and 20 ml. of vitamin stock are added, and the whole made up to 2 liters. This is distributed to culture flasks (50 ml.) or tubes (15 ml.), autoclaved, and allowed to cool. It is then ready for use. For semi-solid nutrient the same nutrient formula is used but is made up to half volume. Ten grams of Difco "Noble" agar (or its equivalent in thoroughly leached agar) are dissolved in one liter of hot water. The agar and nutrient are then mixed, distributed while hot

[2] This is in order not to have to weigh a quantity less than 10 mg. It is easier to dilute and discard than to weigh smaller quantities with sufficient precision.

to flasks or tubes, and autoclaved. In making up this nutrient it is unnecessary to check the acidity as the equilibrium pH is about 5.5, at which point agar solidifies quite satisfactorily. This will not be true of all solutions, however. This nutrient is excellent for most species of roots, for all plant tumor tissues so far studied, for many normal callus cultures, and for many embryos. Hildebrandt and Riker, Bonner, and others have modified the formula for special purposes. The vitamin supplement in particular may need alteration for particular tissues.

Gautheret's solution (1942a, 1950), used extensively in both France and the United States for normal (non-tumorous) tissues, likewise consists of a salt solution, a carbohydrate, and a vitamin supplement. In this case, there are, however, a number of permutations which must be considered. The stock salt solution (Knop solution) is as follows:

$Ca(NO_3)_2$	1.0 g.	KH_2PO_4	0.25 g.
KNO_3	0.25 g.	Water to 1 liter.	
$MgSO_4$	0.25 g.		

A second stock, of trace elements, modified by Gautheret after Berthelot (1934), is as follows:

$Fe_2(SO_4)_3$	50.0 g.	$Ti_2(SO_4)_3$	0.2 g.
$MnSO_4$	2.0 g.	$NiSO_4$	0.05 g.
KI	0.5 g.	$CoCl_3$	0.05 g.
$ZnSO_4$	0.1 g.	$CuSO_4$	0.05 g.
H_3BO_3	0.1 g.	H_3BO_3	0.05 g.
H_2SO_4 (66°Baumé)	1.0 ml.	Water to 1 liter.	

Five other stocks are required.

1. Cysteine-HCl .... 100 mg.   Water 100 ml., autoclave 10 min.
   Thiamine .... 10 mg.   at 18 lb. pressure.

2. Ca-pantothenate ...... 10 mg.   Water 100 ml., autoclave.

3. Biotin .... 10 mg.   Water 100 ml., filter.

4. Inositol .... 1.0 g.   Water 100 ml., autoclave.

5. Naphthalene-acetic acid 10 mg.   Do NOT AUTOCLAVE. Requires no
   30% ethyl alcohol ..... 100 ml.   sterilization.

In making up the five modifications of this solution which are commonly used, ingredients are taken as follows:

Stock	M_1	M_2	M_3	M_4	M_5
Knop solution	100 ml.	100	100	100	100
Berthelot solution	1 ml.	1	1	1	1
Dextrose	30 g.	50	50	50	50
Agar (Noble)	6 g.	6	6	6	6
Cysteine-thiamine	10 ml.	10	10	10	...
Ca-pantothenate	1 ml.	...	...	...	1
Biotin	1 ml.	...	...	...	1
Inositol	10 ml.	...	...	...	...
NAA	3 ml.	1	...	0.5	1
Water	875 ml.	886	887	886	840

Due to the very high acidity of the Berthelot solution, these solutions will all have to be adjusted with 0.1 N NaOH to a pH of 5.7 before autoclaving, otherwise the agar will not solidify. After adjustment they should be distributed to flasks or tubes, autoclaved for 15 minutes at 18 pounds pressure and allowed to cool before use.

For plant tissues, only three additional matters need be discussed. Boll and Street (1951) have concluded that many tissues, particularly roots, when grown on White's solution made up with specially purified salts, may suffer from a deficiency of copper and molybdenum. Copper is present in the Berthelot solution used by Gautheret, but molybdenum is not. Supplements suggested by Boll and Street are prepared as follows: In 100 ml. of water suspend 15 mg. MoO_3 and add 0.1 N NaOH until dissolved. Dilute this 1:1000. This makes a stock containing 0.1 mg. Mo per liter. Dissolve 25 mg. $CuSO_4$ in 100 ml. of water and dilute 1:100. This stock contains 1.0 mg. Cu per liter. One ml. of each of these stocks in a liter of nutrient gives the concentration of Mo and Cu found to be optimal by Boll and Street.

A second modification arises from the work of van Overbeek, Conklin, and Blakeslee (1941, 1942), extended by Caplin and Steward (1948), and others. These authors found that the milk of the coconut, which is a liquid endosperm and hence almost pure protoplasm, when filtered and autoclaved, provides a supplement which, when added to White's nutrient solution, improved the growth of certain tissues, notably a non-cambial strain of tissue from the carrot root. This is comparable to Carrel's embryo juice (Carrel, 1913b) for animal tissues. This is added at a concentration of 30 ml. coconut milk per liter of nutrient. The nature of the beneficial material is unknown, but its high thermal stability indicates that it is not proteinaceous and may be of relatively low molecular weight. It is certainly not necessary for the satisfactory growth of most tissues.

Similarly, an extract of dried brewers' yeast is known, from the early work of White (1932b, 1934a, 1937a) and others, to provide supplementary materials for some tissues. Weigh out 100 mg. of yeast into 500 ml. of water. Boil for one-half hour, centrifuge for 10 minutes at 3000 rpm (about $1000 \times G$), decant, and add to the other nutrient ingredients making up to one liter. The beneficial results are certainly largely attributable to the thiamine and amino acids contained in the yeast, but there may also be other unknown nutrients provided.

It will be noted that with the exception of the unknowns in yeast and in coconut milk, none of which are required by most tissues and for which it is doubtful if real requirements exist for any tissue, all of the ingredients of the above solutions are known and replaceable at will and are under exact control. The nutritional requirements of plant tissues are definitely established in a general way and need only to be further defined in certain details.

The nutritional requirements of animal tissues are unfortunately by no means so clearly established. Here we must proceed from the complex to the simple.

Blood Plasma and Serum

Parker (1950), Fischer (1930), and Cameron (1950) have described in sufficient detail the drawing of blood from the carotid artery of a fowl and the reader is referred to these texts for information. This method gives a fair volume of blood at one drawing. It has the great disadvantages, however, first of requiring a great deal of equipment and personnel, and second of killing the bird at the second bleeding so that uniform samples of blood from a single bird are not available from week to week. We have found bleeding from the heart to be much more satisfactory. While the procedure for doing this is outlined in the accounts of Lewis (1928) and of Buchsbaum and Loosli (1936), we have found it somewhat difficult to follow their directions. Our own procedure will therefore be outlined in some detail.

The equipment required consists of:

> Two 30-ml. syringes provided with No. 18 needles 2 inches long and with two extra needles in reserve
> Four 15-ml. conical centrifuge tubes in ice, stoppered
> One vial of heparin solution 1:1000
> Alcohol, iodine, cotton
> A board for holding the chicken, with tie tapes

A young, healthy cockerel about one year old is kept without food but with adequate water for 24 hours. He is then brought in and tied loosely to the board, with the right side down, head to the left. The left wing is tied back and the feathers removed from the flank. Lewis (1928) gives an elaborate description of the landmarks for locating the heart. In our experience, if the little finger of the right hand (assuming a moderate-sized or small hand!) is placed on the hip bone of the fowl and the hand allowed to rest in a relaxed position, the thumb will describe an arc which passes over the heart. Similarly, if the same finger is placed over the spine at a point directly above the furthest forward extension of this first arc the thumb will again describe an arc passing over the heart. Where these two arcs intersect should be very close to the proper point of entry. The place is recognizable as a soft triangle, the rearward of two such

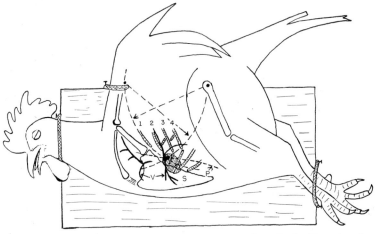

FIGURE 20. Diagram to show the landmarks and method of locating the point of entry for drawing blood from a fowl by direct heart puncture.

triangles. The spot is sterilized with alcohol and marked with iodine. A sterile syringe is taken and the needle inserted into the vial of heparin. Heparin solution is drawn into the syringe, the inner walls wetted and then the solution returned to the vial. The amount remaining on the walls will be sufficient to prevent coagulation of 20 ml. of blood when drawn.[3]

[3] Once the operator becomes expert, heparin can be dispensed with entirely. Its use can also be avoided, if desired, by using a 1-ml. syringe as a "guide," discarding this syringe with the first ml. of blood drawn and replacing it with a fresh, chilled 30-ml. syringe. In this way any juice from tissues injured in inserting the needle will be discarded and no pro-thrombin will be drawn with the final blood supply.

The needle is then inserted into the bird's flank at the previously located spot, being directed slightly rearward and under the sternum. When the needle has been inserted to about half its length, it should be possible to feel the beat of the heart against it. If this is not felt, the needle should be partly withdrawn and the angle altered until the proper point is found. With a little practice the place should be found immediately. Pierce the heart with the needle, being careful not to go too far and pass through the heart. The blood will flow freely into the syringe, forcing the plunger out. It should be unnecessary to use more than a minimum of suction at any time. When about 20 ml. has been drawn, the syringe should be removed from the needle without withdrawing the latter and a new syringe attached. The blood is forced slowly into two of the centrifuge tubes, 10 ml. per tube. The tubes are returned to the ice. When a full supply has been accumulated the tubes are centrifuged briefly—5 minutes at 2000 rpm $(700 \times G)$ is enough. The plasma is drawn off with a chilled pipette, being careful not to disturb the packed erythrocytes, and is transferred to small, paraffined storage tubes, usually not more than 5 ml. per tube, and stored in the refrigerator. Such plasma will keep for months. Lyophilized plasma which can be purchased commercially (Difco, Microbiological Associates) is satisfactory for most cell cultures, but according to Fell and Mellanby (1952) and Carpenter (1942) cannot be used successfully for organ cultures, which they believe require freshly prepared plasma.

During the early part of the bleeding operation the bird will not struggle, but when about 30 ml. have been drawn there is a moment when he is likely to react violently. If he is held firmly at this moment no harm will be done and the convulsion will not be repeated. Another 10 or 20 ml. can be safely drawn. If the bird is not firmly held, however, the heart may be torn and the bird will die.

If this operation is successfully carried out the bird can be returned to his cage and fed immediately and will suffer no serious injury. We had one cockerel which was bled in this way at two-week intervals for more than a year before he was finally killed in a fight with another bird. During that time we had a constant supply of blood, more than a liter in all, which, in all those factors which have a hereditary origin, was entirely uniform. Serum can be prepared from such plasma by adding enough thromboplastic material (embryo juice, for example) to bring about clotting and then breaking up the clot with a sterile glass rod, after which the supernatant serum can be drawn off. Many workers, whose laboratories are attached to large hospitals, prefer to use human placental-cord serum. Blood is either drawn from the umbilical vein with a hypodermic or is merely allowed to drain directly from the cut cord into a suitable tube. It is allowed to clot, and the supernatant serum drawn off after syneresis, filtered to render it aseptic, and stored in the refrigerator. Horse serum and filtered ox serum are also available commercially, both liquid and lyophilized, and will be found satisfactory for most purposes.

Embryo Extract

For most purposes chick embryos will be most easily available. A series of 10- to 12-day incubated eggs are opened (see under "Setting Up Cultures") and the embryos removed into a sterile dish. Five to seven embryos are dropped into a 20-ml. syringe, heads and all, and the plunger inserted. Earle (Evans, Earle, *et al.*, 1951), Hanks (1952), and Carpenter (1947) insert a fine-mesh stainless steel screen in the syringe but we find this unnecessary, though perhaps giving a somewhat finer pulp. The mouth of the syringe is inserted into a 15-ml. centrifuge tube and the plunger pushed down. The embryos will be forced through the opening and will be finely triturated without excessive destruction of the cells themselves. About 4 ml. of juice will be obtained from each embryo. A volume of salt-dextrose solution (Tyrode, Gey, Earle, White) is added, equal to the volume of embryo material, the whole mixed thoroughly with a sterile glass rod and set aside over night. The brei is then centrifuged at 3000 rpm ($1000 \times G$) for 10 minutes and the supernatant decanted and either filtered or stored immediately in the refrigerator. We find this method more satisfactory than any of the grinding or chopping methods described elsewhere. It is certainly simpler, involves less manipulation, and hence danger of contamination. Each batch of embryo extract and of blood as well should be tested bacteriologically before being used. While this gives an embryo extract which is quite satisfactory for most purposes, a still more active preparation can be obtained if the raw juice is frozen and thawed one or more times before centrifuging. Some workers also prefer to incubate the brei and salt-dextrose solution together at 37.5°C. for 10 to 24 hours before centrifuging. Embryo extract, either liquid or lyophilized, can also be purchased commercially.

Unfortunately, embryos of mice, rats, rabbits, pigs, beef, and other mammals, while physiologically quite satisfactory, are too fibrous to be treated by passing through a syringe. They must either be ground in a tissue grinder, cut up with knives or scissors, or divided in some other way. Special grinders with glass barrels and Teflon (plastic) pistons are available for use with small embryos. Beef embryos can be obtained from a slaughter house with the amniotic sac intact and brought to the laboratory in sterile saline. An embryo about 5 to 6 inches in length will be suitable. In the laboratory the sac is opened and the embryo removed. This can be ground briefly in a Waring Blendor. If grinding is stopped soon enough this gives a fairly satisfactory result, although a too prolonged grinding may result in a milky suspension which cannot be cleared by centrifugation. One 5-inch beef embryo will provide several hundred milliliters of clear juice, enough for many weeks of work in the average laboratory.

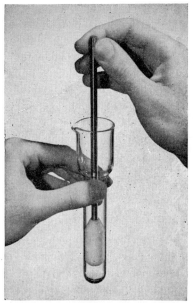

FIGURE 21. Method of using the TenBroeck-Potter tissue grinder with Teflon plunger. This is a very effective grinder and should be used for exacting work, although simple passage through the orifice of a hypodermic syringe will suffice for most routine purposes. Compare with Figure 19. (Courtesy of Arthur H. Thomas Co., Philadelphia)

Lewis and Lewis (1911b) and more recently Doljanski (Hoffman and Doljanski, 1939; Doljanski and Hoffman, 1943; Hoffman, Dingwall, and Andrus, 1951) have shown that tissue bouillons from adult tissues provide fairly satisfactory nutrient materials. Chicken leg or breast muscle, veal muscle, beef heart, etc., are cut to pieces a centimeter or less on a side, boiled, and the fluid decanted and used as a nutrient. Such bouillons should be made as nearly fat-free as possible, since fatty materials are generally growth-inhibiting.

It has recently been found that these embryo extracts can be cleared and sterilized by filtration. Filtering may be through any of the various types of bacteriological filters—Berkefeld or Chamberland (diatomaceous earth), Selas (porcelain), Seitz (asbestos pads), or sintered glass. The use of most of these filters is well known and need not be repeated here. Of them all we prefer the Selas candle. Filtration under vacuum alone is very slow, requiring about 48 hours for 100 ml. of juice. This can be greatly accelerated by using a pressure filter. Bryant, Earle, and Peppers (1953) report (and we have verified) that embryo extract can be filtered as rapidly as water alone if first treated with 0.01 per cent hyaluronidase.

The method of using Selas filters is not universally known and has not been described in detail elsewhere so far as I am aware. It is of sufficient importance to deserve attention here.

The Selas porcelain filter is of the same general type as the Berkefeld or Chamberland candle, but because of its special method of manufacture the pores are all within a narrow range of diameters—hence it does not require standardization and is free of possible leaks. Although made in several sizes and pore diameters, the ⅝ by 2-inch candle of ultra-fine porosity (03) will be most commonly used in cell culture work. This is sold with a special double-end rubber stopper of a size about equivalent to a No. 7 and a Pyrex glass mantle which permits its effective use down to about 3 ml. of fluid. This stopper can be placed directly in a standard filter flask of the Erlenmeyer type. We prefer to use the "Mudd column" originally designed for filtering bacteriological preparations. The Selas stopper is too small to fit this column satisfactorily but is rendered snug by covering it with a double thickness of Gooch-crucible tubing.

We have found it unsatisfactory to sterilize this equipment assembled. We use the following procedure. If filtration is to be carried out from the outside of the candle inward, utilizing the larger outer surface (this is the standard method), the filter candle is inserted in the stopper, candle up, and the Gooch tubing added. This is laid on the corner of a 10 by 10-inch piece of wrapping paper or muslin and the corner folded around it once. The glass mantle is then laid alongside, the wrapping completed, and the whole tied. The upper mouth and side tubulation of the Mudd column are closed with cotton plugs, the side plug being snug enough so as not to be easily forced out by changes in air pressure. The outlet is provided with a piece of pure gum rubber or silicone tubing about 3 inches long into which a small size filling-bell is inserted. The bell is likewise plugged with cotton, the tube bent so that the bell lies alongside the graduated column, and the whole wrapped in paper and tied. Both column and filter are sterilized by autoclaving at 15 pounds pressure for 10 minutes, followed by drying under vacuum, as in handling all equipment containing rubber.

When it is to be used, the Mudd column is unwrapped and set up in a standard burette support. The filter mantle is unwrapped and taken in the left hand, and the unwrapping is continued to expose the candle; this is picked up with the right hand, grasping only the stopper with the sterile paper, the filter is inserted in the mantle, and then quickly introduced into the top of the column. The vacuum tube is attached, being sure that an adequate trap is introduced between the column and vacuum source (this is especially important if a water pump is used as source of vacuum), a clamp is placed on the rubber outlet tube, and the apparatus is ready for use (Fig. 22G). The material to be filtered is poured into the mantle and the vacuum started.

In practice we find it almost impossible to control the rate of change from atmospheric pressure to vacuum and back

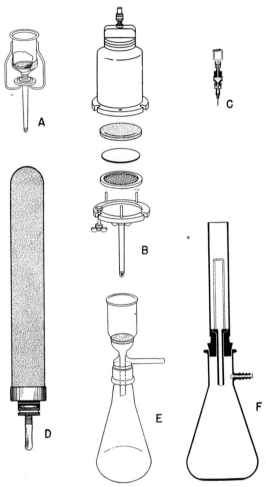

FIGURE 22. Filters and their use. The filters illustrated are: A, the Seitz filter in its simplest form using an asbestos pad and suitable for filtration under suction only; B, a modification of the Seitz filter adapted for use with either suction or pressure or both, hence permitting rapid filtration; C, a micro-Seitz or "Swinney" filter for filtering very small volumes of fluid, using a standard hypodermic syringe as the reservoir and source of pressure; D, the "Mandler" filter made of diatomaceous earth; E, an all-glass filter using a membrane of sintered porous glass as the filtration unit; F, G, H, and I, the "Selas" porous porcelain filter candle. In F this candle is

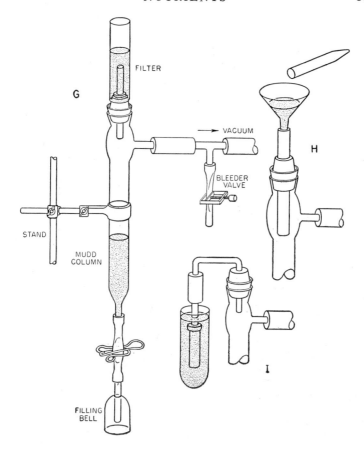

FILTER

G

→ VACUUM

H

BLEEDER
VALVE

STAND

MUDD
COLUMN

I

FILLING
BELL

FIGURE 22. (*Continued*)

mounted for use in a standard filter flask, while in G and I the Mudd filter column is used. All of these are suitable for sterilization of nutrients. A, B, and C have the advantage of great ruggedness and simplicity and the filter membrane is disposable but the asbestos pads may, for some work, prove chemically objectionable; D is of uneven porosity and requires rigorous calibration; E is simple, reliable, and chemically irreproachable but somewhat fragile and must be cleaned by acid washing. The Selas filter, either candle or funnel, is chemically acceptable, of reliable porosity, rugged and can be cleaned by firing at high temperature (600°C.) followed by washing. We believe it to be the best of these filters for general use. (Figure prepared in part by the Selas Corporation)

again directly at the vacuum source (water pump, vacuum pump, vacuum line) gradually enough to prevent the protective plug in the side tubulation from being forced either into the vacuum line or into the column, either of which would destroy the sterility of the system. To obviate this we place a T-tube in the vacuum line, the stem of which is provided with a soft rubber tubulation and a screw clamp. The vacuum is started with this tubulation open. Then the screw clamp is closed gradually. Vacuum should be maintained below 250 mm. mercury to avoid boiling, particularly when filtering solutions containing bicarbonate. After filtration is complete this tubulation is opened gradually with the vacuum still on, the latter being shut off only after the system has been fully opened.

Vitamin solutions, bicarbonate, sugar, and the like, will filter very quickly, 100 ml. in less than 5 minutes. Viscous preparations such as serum or embryo extract will be much slower unless treated with some agent, such as hyaluronidase.

The procedure for cleaning filters must also be described. The candles are removed from their stoppers as soon as they have been used, rinsed thoroughly in tap water, and then stood stem up in a 500-ml. beaker of dilute hypochlorite solution. They should not be allowed to dry out. When a number have been accumulated the fluid is poured off, and the beaker and filters are filled with concentrated H_2SO_4 plus a trace of $NaNO_3$ or HNO_3. This is simmered on a water bath under a hood for one-half hour. The acid is decanted and the filters rinsed thoroughly in tap water. The filters are inverted in 500-ml. filter flasks, the flasks attached to a vacuum line with a large trap (a manifold can be used if several filters are to be cleaned at once), thistle tubes or funnels are attached to the filters, these are filled with distilled water, and suction is started. About a liter of distilled water should be drawn through each candle. The cleaning solution followed by rinsing will remove most soluble residues from the pores of the candles. The candles are then removed, all water is shaken out and they are placed for a few hours in a drying oven to remove all moisture. They are then placed in a shallow metal tray in a muffle furnace where they are brought to 600°C. and held there for a minimum of one-half hour. They should be allowed to cool slowly to avoid cracking. This treatment will completely incinerate any insoluble organic residues. The candles are then again attached to the vacuum line and a liter of single distilled water, followed by 500 ml. of double distilled water flushed through each, after which they are ready to be dried, wrapped, and sterilized for use again.

Although this procedure is somewhat tedious it is technically simple and highly effective, and the result is irreproachable. Seitz filters may be objectionable because of the constituents of the filter pads, sintered glass filters are fragile and cannot be incinerated, Berkefeld and Chamberland filters are uneven in quality and prone to leaks and irregularities. The Selas filter has none of these objections.

Salt Solutions

All of the older tissue culture nutrients were built around the solutions of Ringer (1886), Locke (1895, 1901), or Tyrode (1910), and the reader is referred to Parker's book for a full and adequate discussion of their preparation. These solutions, however, were not originally designed for this purpose and do not bear a very close resemblance to the ionic constitution of body fluids. Theoretically better solutions have been developed more recently. Two of these will be described, that of Earle (1943), based on the solution developed by Gey and Gey (1936), and that of White (1946, 1949), developed independently.

Earle's Salt Solution.—

NaCl	6.8 g.	$MgSO_4 \cdot 7H_2O$	0.2 g.
KCl	0.4 g.	$NaH_2PO_4 \cdot H_2O$	0.125 g.
$CaCl_2 \cdot 2H_2O$	0.2 g.	Dextrose	1.0 g.

These ingredients should be dissolved successively in 800 ml. of double distilled water, and autoclaved. Two and two-tenths grams of $NaHCO_3$ are dissolved in 200 ml. of water containing 25 mg. phenol red, filtered through a Selas candle, and saturated with CO_2, bubbling through a plugged and sterile pipette. The two solutions are then mixed aseptically and the solution is ready for use.

White's Salt Solution.—White's solution makes use of three stock solutions:

1.
NaCl	14.000 g.	Distribute to tubes in 10-ml.
KCl	0.750 g.	aliquots and autoclave.
$MgSO_4$	0.550 g.	
$Ca(NO_3)_2 \cdot H_2O$	0.420 g.	
Water	100 ml.	

2.
$Fe(NO_3)_3 \cdot 9H_2O$	11 mg.	Distribute and autoclave.
Water	400 ml.	

3.
Dextrose	17.000 g.	Saturate with CO_2, filter through
$NaHCO_3$	2.200 g.	a Selas candle. Store in the
$Na_2HPO_4 \cdot 12H_2O$	0.580 g.	refrigerator. This should have
KH_2PO_4	0.104 g.	a pH of ca. 7.4.
Phenol red	0.010 g.	
Water	100 ml.	

These stocks are all 20 times the concentration required in the final nutrient. A solution is made up for use by adding 5 ml. of each of these stocks to 85 ml. of sterile water. The same stocks can be used in making up more complex nutrients.

Synthetic Nutrients

Vogelaar and Erlichman (1933), Baker (1936), and Baker and Ebeling (1939) have described nutrients made up largely of defined materials which they designate as "synthetic." These, however, contain blood serum and other organic unknowns, and are therefore not truly defined. Their preparation is discussed by Parker and will not be repeated here. Fischer has gone a step further in reducing the unknowns to a basic residue by employing plasma and embryo juices which have previously been subjected to dialysis against a dextrose-Ringer solution until they will no longer support cell proliferation (1941a, b). These are considered "biologically inert." They are still unknowns, however, and the work of White and Lasfargues (1949), Barski et al. (1951), and Harris (1952a) casts some doubt on their being truly inert. White (1946, 1949), Fischer (1941b), and later Morgan, Morton, and Parker (1950) have developed fully defined, completely synthetic nutrients which, while not capable of supporting unlimited growth of animal tissues, are nevertheless excellent protective solutions on the basis of which more complete nutrients may be built. Two of these, that of Fischer and that of White, will be discussed in detail.

Fischer's Nutrient.—Fischer has developed a number of solutions for supplementing his basic dialyzed plasma-dialyzed embryo-juice substratum. Two of these may be cited. The first (Fischer, 1948) contained 49 ingredients. This was later simplified by Fischer, Astrup, Ehrensvärd, and Oehlenschläger (1948). It is designated solution "V-614," and is available from Microbiological Associates, Inc., Bethesda, Maryland. It consists of:

NaCl	7500 mg.	DL-threonine	24 mg.
Glucose	2000 mg.	DL-isoleucine	20 mg.
NaHCO$_3$	1000 mg.	L-leucine	18 mg.
KCl	200 mg.	DL-phenylalanine	14 mg.
CaCl$_2$	200 mg.	L-histidine HCl	10 mg.
MgCl$_2$	100 mg.	L-cystine	10 mg.
Glutamine	250 mg.	Glutathione	10 mg.
Fructose-diphosphate	200 mg.	L-arginine HCl	4 mg.
Na$_2$HPO$_4$	50 mg.	L-tryptophane	4 mg.
L-lysine 2HCl	30 mg.	Water	1000 ml.
DL-valine	28 mg.		

No special instructions are given for preparing this solution. Ehrensvärd, Fischer, and Stjernholm (1949) have further simplified solution "V-614" as follows:

NaCl	8000 mg.	Ca-fructose-1-6 diphos-	
NaHCO$_3$	1000 mg.	phate	300 mg.
KCl	200 mg.	Glutamine	250 mg.
CaCl$_2$	200 mg.	Glycine	250 mg.
MgCl$_2$·6H$_2$O	100 mg.	Cystine	15 mg.
NaH$_2$PO$_4$·H$_2$O	50 mg.	Hypoxanthine	7 mg.
Glucose	1000 mg.	Water	1000 ml.

They report that this is as effective in supplementing the dialyzed substratum as is the more complex nutrient. Neither, however, will support growth without some organic supplementation.

White's Nutrient.—White's nutrient solution for animal tissues has been developed by a careful consideration of the information on cellular nutrition made available, over the past two decades, as a result of a great many investigations with bacteria, molds, invertebrates, and mammals, including man. It is predicated on the assumption that the basic requirements of all cells will be found to be more or less alike, that findings in one field can, with conscious reservations, be tentatively extended to other fields, and that it should therefore be possible to set up a reasoned formula, resorting to analysis of complex nutrients of known effectiveness only for the purpose of corroborating empirical findings. Thus the salt solution (already given) was developed to provide as nearly as possible the ionic constitution of adult human blood serum, but it was also recognized that in spite of the dominant place which sodium chloride plays in the ionic composition of blood there are other anions besides the chloride which may be important. For that reason sulfates and nitrates, which are not included in most of the classic salt solutions, have been introduced in substitution for some of the chlorides of the solutions of Locke, Ringer, Tyrode, etc., and the phosphates and carbonates have been subjected to special scrutiny.

Similarly, although dextrose is employed in the solution as energy source, it is not forgotten that sucrose has regularly proved superior to dextrose in the nutrition of plant tissues (White, 1940a, b; Burström, 1941a, b; Dormer and Street, 1949; Street and Lowe, 1950; Street and McGregor, 1952; Street, 1950) owing to its participation in the processes of phosphorylation. Hence this and other sugars must be given careful consideration. Both vitamins and inorganic trace elements have been incorporated, in so far as our information gives us justification for doing so. The resulting nutrient is complex, probably more so than will ultimately prove to be necessary, and it is not completely satisfactory. This may be due to deficiencies, to imbalances, or possibly to superfluities and toxicities which must be eliminated by further experience.

The salts and carbohydrate have already been outlined. The amino acid solution is based on the formula of Rose (1932) for nutrition of rats, dogs, and man, and modified by Madden and Whipple (1940; Madden et al., 1943) for use in the treatment of shock in dogs and man. It has further been supplemented to include the transaminating amino acids and also glycine, which is known to be nonessential for man and rats but essential for chickens (Almquist and Grau, 1944). It is prepared as follows:

Dissolve successively in 80 ml. of water:

L-lysine HCl	312 mg.	DL-isoleucine	208 mg.
DL-methionine	260 mg.	DL-phenylalanine	100 mg.
DL-threonine	260 mg.	L-leucine	312 mg.
DL-valine	260 mg.	L-tryptophane	80 mg.
L-arginine HCl	156 mg.	L-glutamic acid	280 mg.
L-histidine HCl	52 mg.	L-aspartic acid	120 mg.
L-proline	100 mg.	L-cystine	30 mg.
glycine (amino-acetic acid)	200 mg.		

Phenol red, 10 ml. of solution containing 10 mg. phenol red per 100 ml.

These are arranged approximately in descending order of solubility. The concentration of cystine is slightly above its saturation value in cold water but will dissolve in the presence of other amino acids on heating. Glutamic and aspartic acids are soluble at these levels but go into solution very slowly. When fully dissolved, the pH should be adjusted to 7.4, which will require about 3 ml. of N NaOH. The whole is then made up to 100 ml. volume, distributed in 10-ml. aliquots and filtered. It should be stored in the refrigerator.

The vitamin stock solutions are likewise rather complex.

AC-Stock.—

GROUP A

β-carotene	10 mg.	This requires no sterilization.
Vitamin A (free)	10 mg.	
C_2H_5OH	100 ml.	

GROUP B

Ascorbic acid	10 mg.	Filter and distribute.
Glutathione	20 mg.	
Cysteine HCl	20 mg.	
Water	100 ml.	

GROUP C

Phenol red	10 mg.	Distribute and autoclave.
Water	100 ml.	

Mix aseptically 2 ml. of A, 10 ml. of B, 2 ml. of C, and 86 ml. of water. Adjust to pH 7.4 with sterile 0.1 N NaOH, distribute, and store in the refrigerator.

B-Stock.—

GROUP B₁

Thiamine HCl	10 mg.	This should be sterilized by
Riboflavin	10 mg.	filtration through a Selas
Ca-pantothenate	10 mg.	candle, distributed, and stored
d-biotin	10 mg.	in the refrigerator.
Pyridoxin HCl	10 mg.	
Nicotinic acid	10 mg.	
Inositol	10 mg.	
β-alanine	10 mg.	
Choline	100 mg.	
Water	100 ml.	

GROUP FA

Folic acid	10 mg.	This should be sterilized by
NaHCO₃	10 mg.	filtration.
Water	100 ml.	

GROUP B₁₂

Fifteen mg. of vitamin B_{12} are dissolved in 100 ml. of water, distributed in 10-ml. aliquots, and autoclaved. Store in the refrigerator.

The final nutrient is made by mixing aseptically and in order 70 ml. of sterile water, 5 ml. each of salt solution (1), $Fe(NO_3)_3$ solution (2), dextrose-buffer (3), amino acids (4), AC-stock (5), B-stock (6), and B_{12} (7). It is essential that this order be preserved, for if the phosphate and/or bicarbonate are mixed with other ingredients before the water is added there will be formed insoluble precipitates which will not redissolve and which will leave a much too alkaline, toxic solution. If the instructions are properly carried out, the resulting solution will be a clear pale red in color, with a pH of about 7.4, and will support prolonged survival of many animal tissues. It is probable that some of the vitamins listed will prove to be non-essential and that many concentrations will be altered after further study. Nevertheless, this has proved to be an excellent, fully-defined synthetic base line from which to work.

It is interesting to note that the defined nutrient developed independently by Morgan, Morton, and Parker (1950) is essentially identical with this solution except for the inclu-

sion of the purines, of "Tween," and of a number of substances in what are probably functionally duplicate forms.
Thus the solution of Morgan, Morton, and Parker contains
both nicotinic acid and nicotinamide, both pyridoxin and
pyridoxal, and certain other duplications. It is doubtful if
these constitute real functional differences.

These then are the major nutrients which will be used in
cell culture studies.

Chapter 6

TYPES OF CULTURES

T ISSUE cultures, whether plant or animal, fall into four
main classes: (1) hanging-drop, (2) flask, (3) test-tube,
and (4) watch-glass cultures.

Hanging-Drop Cultures

These are the simplest in point of equipment required.
They also permit the greatest precision of optical study, such
as the use of oil immersion and phase contrast objectives.
But they have the serious drawbacks of very poor control
of nutrient variables and of extreme tedium in the maintenance of cultures due to the need for very frequent subculturing. Hanging-drop cultures will be made on cover glasses
suspended over either hollow-ground slides, pierced slides,
van Tiegham cells, or small watch glasses.

In the simplest procedure a series of perhaps a half-dozen
22 by 22-mm. No. 1 cover glasses, scrupulously clean, are
laid out on a sheet of black glass or plastic on the culture
table. A single drop of nutrient, either synthetic or containing embryo extract, is placed at the center of each glass and
spread over an area not to exceed one half the diameter of
the cavity of the slide. Bits of tissue (animal tissues, root
tips, cambium, sporelings, mammalian eggs, limb primordia)
are then placed in the nutrient drops. If plasma is to be
added, it is done at this time, and the whole quickly mixed
with the end of the pipette, with a glass rod, or a platinum

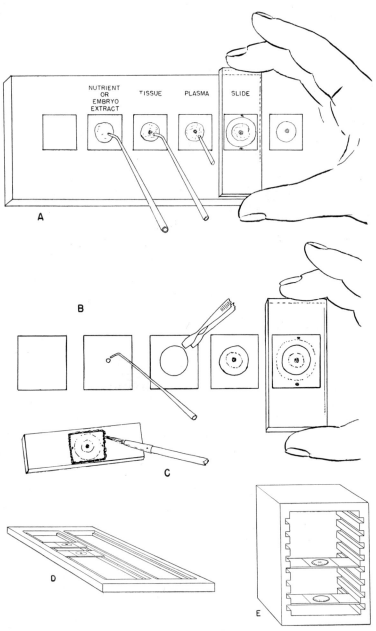

Figure 23. (*Explanation on opposite page*)

spatula. Two drops of vaseline are applied with a glass rod, brush, or piece of stick to a slide, at the two sides of the cavity. This is repeated until a number of slides equal to that of the cover slips is ready. A slide is then inverted over each cover glass and pressed down firmly. The vaseline will thus attach the cover glass to the slide. The slides are carefully lifted and placed on a suitable rack (Fig. 23) for about one-half hour while other cultures are being prepared. During this time the culture itself will become firmly attached to the glass, and, in the case of plasma cultures, the plasma will coagulate. The slides can then be inverted by a quick centrifugal motion which does not disturb the drop of nutrient, and the cover is sealed with a hot paraffin-vaseline mixture (3:1) applied with a brush, after which the slides are ready for observation or for the incubator.

For cultures for which observation is not to be continued for more than a few days, this is an entirely satisfactory procedure. It is, however, difficult to remove such cover slips from the slide without cracking the cover, disturbing

---

FIGURE 23. A, Method of preparing hanging-drop cultures of animal tissues. Six clean 22 by 22-mm. cover glasses are laid out on a block of glass or plastic. A drop of nutrient is first placed on each glass and spread in a uniform circle about 5 mm. in diameter. A bit of tissue is then placed in each drop and a drop of plasma (if this is to be used) is added, stirring thoroughly but without spreading the drop further. A hollow-ground slide is then inverted over each cover slip, drops of vaseline serving to attach the slide and cover. The slides are then transferred to a storage rack (D or E) either in the original position for a period of settling or as permanent "sitting drops," and to permit coagulation of the clot (if any), or are inverted so as to place the cover glass uppermost. In either case the cover must be ringed with paraffin vaseline mixture (C) before being placed in the incubator.

B, Method of preparing Maximow double cover-slip cultures. This differs from the simple hanging drop culture only in that the culture is prepared on a small detachable cover slip (usually round) attached to the larger rectangular cover which rests directly on the slide. For these cultures 35 by 40-mm. covers are usually employed.

C, Method of sealing cover with paraffin-vaseline mixture (see Fig. 19 for equipment for this purpose).

D, A tray for storage and incubation of slide cultures.

E, A type of rack used in some laboratories for storage of slide cultures.

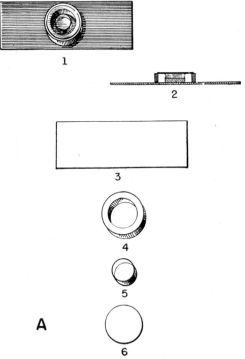

FIGURE 24. A, A simple "sitting drop" assembly designed by Roger J. Gautheret for the cultivation of excised root-tips but equally suitable for animal tissue cultures. It consists of an ordinary 1 by 3-inch slide, a low glass, plastic, or metal ring about 20 mm. outside diameter and 3-5 mm. high (van Tiegham cell), a disk of glass 7 mm. in diameter (about 1 mm. less in thickness than the height of the ring), and a 22-mm. round cover glass. The disk has its edges optically ground. The ring is cemented to the slide. A drop of water is placed in the middle of the cavity and the disk set here so that it is attached by capillarity. The culture is made on top of this disk in a drop of nutrient sufficient in amount so that when the cover slip is added it will make contact with the nutrient. There is thus established an optically continuous system between the top of the cover

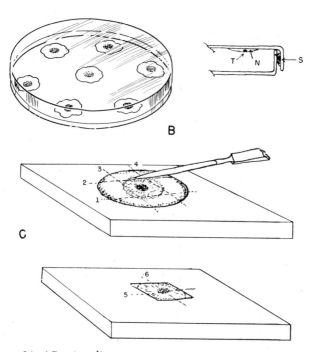

FIGURE 24. (*Continued*)

slip and the bottom of the slide, permitting the use of high-powered objectives. This unit has two advantages over other "sitting drop" slides, first that the drop, sitting on top of a column, cannot possibly slip sideways and make contact with the ring, and second that a relatively large volume of air is enclosed around the drop and column providing satisfactory conditions for tissue respiration. (From Gautheret, 1935)

B, A Petri dish carrying seven cultures prepared according to Barski's method. *T*, tissue; *N*, nutrient drop; *S*, string soaked in hot paraffin, serving to seal the Petri dish (see text). (Redrawn from Wirth *et al.*, 1947)

C, Method of cutting up a plasma clot, such as a hanging drop culture, in preparing four subcultures (see text).

the drop, or otherwise deranging the culture. For cultures in which it is desired to renew nutrient, to make subcultures, or to make microchemical studies, the double cover-slip method of Maximow (1925) is superior. In this method a large cover slip, usually 30 by 35 mm., is laid out as before. A fairly large drop of sterile distilled water is applied and a 20-mm. round cover slip or a 16-mm. square one is placed on this. The water is gauged to be just sufficient to hold the second cover slip to the other firmly, by capillarity. The culture is then placed on the smaller slip. The rest of the procedure is the same as before. In transferring or otherwise manipulating these cultures, the small slip may be floated free merely by adding an excess of sterile water or saline at the side.

Both of these methods, using hollow-ground slides, have the optical disadvantage imposed by the curvature of the cavity. This may be obviated by the use of flat slides bearing metal or glass rings (see Lewis) or pierced slides, either of glass, metal, or plastic. One of the most satisfactory (White, 1943a, Fig. 27) is a pierced slide with both top and bottom routed out around the opening to take a square cover glass at a level slightly below that of the slide proper. A No. 2 cover slip is attached with vaseline to the lower side of the slide, forming an optically flat bottom to the closed chamber. The culture itself is set up exactly as described for use on a hollow-ground slide. The cavity can be opened for changing nutrient, making subcultures, and the like, by removing the bottom cover glass without disturbing the slip carrying the culture. For specially precise optical studies, as with phase-contrast equipment, the pierced slide can be made thin enough so that the culture drop will make contact with both top and bottom cover slip, thereby providing a continuous optical medium, while the margins of the drop provide the necessary aeration. This is what Gey terms a "sitting-drop culture." A somewhat more versatile version of this same type of culture was described by Gautheret in 1935.

In place of pierced slides Lewis has used low metal rings, dipped in paraffin, and applied to plane slides. The "Raschig rings" sold for use in distillation columns can be very easily ground flat on the ends on a wheel or a plate of glass coated with carborundum powder, and make excellent small chambers; or one can purchase the more expensive "van Tiegham rings" sold for making cultures of fungi.

Barski's "Formvar" Method

Many variants of the hanging-drop method have been tried. Two of these, both emanating from the Institut Pasteur in Paris, are worth mentioning. The first is particularly valuable for brief observation of numerous cultures such as might be used in school demonstrations. On the inner surface of the cover of an ordinary Petri dish are placed seven rather large drops of plasma, six around the edge, a seventh in the middle. Cultures are made in these as for cover-slip cultures. The inside of the Petri dish is then inverted into the part carrying the cultures and a piece of twine dipped in hot paraffin is run into the space between to seal the vessel. The vessel can be opened simply by pulling this string. The dish is then placed in the incubator. The whole can be inverted on the stage of the microscope for low-power observation. Subcultures can be made from such cultures. This method has the possible disadvantage that a contamination of one of the seven cultures may eventually spread to all. In addition, subculturing is rather clumsy.

The second method is a refinement, growing out of the investigators' interest in electron microscopy. Barski prepares a 0.2 per cent solution of polyvinyl formal [1] in ethylene

[1] "Formvar," Grade #15–95. Obtainable from the Shawinigan Products Corp., New York.

dichloride (Barski and Maurin, 1948; Barski and Manigault, 1951). This is deposited drop by drop onto cold sterile Ringer's solution, where each drop spreads in a very thin, circular film about 1 cm. in diameter and hardens. Or a larger film can be prepared on a slide, stripped off, and cut into the desired size and shape. We have found it more satisfactory to make a 3 per cent solution of Formvar in acetic acid. This is spread on one side of a warmed slide where it dries quickly. The Formvar layer is then cut with a sharp knife and under sterile water is stripped off the glass. A long ribbon 15 by 50 mm. can thus be prepared which can be cut into the desired pieces. These films are transferred with fine forceps to a watch glass of sterile water or Ringer solution. In making cultures a disk or square of Formvar is transferred to a cover glass, or seven disks may be placed in a Petri dish (Barski's procedure). With a very fine, pointed pipette filled with liquid nutrient (serum-embryo-extract, Tyrode solution, synthetic nutrient, or any other desired nutrient), the disk is punctured and a large drop of nutrient forced under the disk, causing it to bulge. The bit of tissue to be cultured is then placed on top of the Formvar. Cells will migrate out onto this surface and are nourished by diffusion through the plastic. The entire disk can be slipped off for washing, for transfer *in toto* to a new mount, for fixing and staining, or it can be cut up and used in making subcultures. This appears to be a very valuable procedure, deserving of more attention than it has had to date.

Disks of perforated cellophane of the type developed by Evans and Earle (1947; see below) for flask cultures can be substituted for Barski's Formvar, but since they are much heavier, cultures are best made under the cellophane rather than on top of it. They therefore offer little advantage over hanging drops without overlay except that they can be removed for washing, subculturing, and the like.

Hanging drops such as have been described are regularly employed for short-term studies of animal cell cultures of all sorts. They also form the bases for many of the long-term cultures of Carrel, Fischer, and their followers, particularly before the development of the Carrel flask. Plant materials such as embryos, root and stem tips (White, 1932a, 1933a), intercalary meristems, and algal sporelings have also been grown by this method. Its chief drawbacks are its relative tediousness where the nutrient must often be changed, and the rather rapid and uncontrollable changes in total concentration, pH, oxygen tension, ionic levels, and the like, to which a small drop of fluid exposed with a large surface area in contact both with a glass surface and even a saturated atmosphere is inevitably subject.

Transferring Cultures

With liquid nutrients it is impossible to subculture hanging-drop cultures of animal cells except by Barski's Formvar method or with Earle's cellophane. With plasma clots, however, subcultures can be made; in fact, this method served Carrel and Ebeling for their thirty-year cultivation of chick fibroblasts. The cover slip, Petri dish, or other container carrying a well-grown plasma-clot culture (usually about ten days old) is placed, clot up, on a raised block and the fluid supernatant (if any) withdrawn. The thin edges are trimmed off and discarded. For this, Parker (1950) recommends cataract knives, which are expensive. Bits of razor blade held firmly in a hemostat, or Bard-Parker knives can be used. The important thing is not to tear the culture. With a cataract knife the cut should be made with the knife laid across the culture with the handle low and the blade tilted at a slight angle (about 10°) from the perpendicular. A quick but very slight forward-backward motion will cut without tearing, after which the knife should be lifted away, not drawn away. The same applies to razor blades in hemostats. With Bard-Parker knives, a small round-edged blade should be used and the blade rocked across the culture. Any of these methods will make a clean cut. The edges are trimmed by four such cuts, leaving a square of dense growth with the original explant in the center. This square may then be divided into two or four pieces, depending on how well it has grown. It should not be divided into more than four pieces since in subculturing, smaller bits will seldom grow satisfactorily. These bits should be picked up on the knife blade, transferred to a new cover slip, laid out flat without rolled edges, and then covered with fresh plasma. All these operations must be carried out in such a way that the tissue will not dry out, and with as little crushing as possible.

Flask Cultures

In flask cultures the tissues are maintained either in liquid media or on some solid or semi-solid substratum. For purposes of discussion, cultivation in which the tissues are attached to the glass, even though submerged in liquid, will be considered to fall into the latter category. Cultures in liquid have been mostly of two kinds. Excised roots are grown floating on a liquid nutrient (White, 1934a, 1943a). The most generally accepted practice is to use 125-ml. Erlenmeyer flasks with 50 ml. of nutrient. A bit of root, usually about 10–15 mm. long, is inoculated into the flask with a bacteriological loop. Here it will float on the surface of the liquid and grow. It can be cut into one or more pieces after an acceptable period, usually a week, and the desired subcultures made by simple transfer. For cutting, Heyman nose-and-throat scissors are excellent. Such root cultures have been maintained for more than twenty years. Roots have also been grown in Petri dishes (Bonner and Addicott, 1937), which are difficult to handle without slopping, and in 25 by

100-mm. test tubes (White, unpublished), in which no more than 20 ml. of nutrient can be supplied.

Animal viruses have also been grown in Erlenmeyer flasks by a method developed by Maitland and Maitland (1928),

FIGURE 25. Two 125-ml. Erlenmeyer flasks containing (left) a plant callus culture and (right) an excised plant root. The same sort of flasks can be used for cultivation of animal viruses by the Maitland (1928) tissue suspension method.

perfected by Li and Rivers (1930), and recently revived in various forms for cultivation of poliomyelitis and other viruses (Enders, 1948). A "nutrient" is prepared by cutting a suitable tissue, such as rabbit testicle, into small bits and suspending them in a salt-dextrose solution, such as Tyrode. Virus is then supplied by transfer of a small amount of fluid from a previous culture. The tissue does not "grow" or increase in amount but gradually breaks down. It serves for some days, however, as a living substratum on which the virus can multiply, and transfers to fresh flasks can be made at weekly intervals (Feller, Enders, and Weller, 1940). Interest here rests not in the tissue but in the virus, and this method, carried on in test tubes, Erlenmeyer flasks, or other bottles, has proved highly useful. A somewhat comparable method has been used by Osgood and others for relatively short-term cultivation of blood cells and bone marrow.

If, however, the primary interest lies in long-term cultivation and observation of living cells, more specialized methods must be used. The Carrel flask, although expensive and somewhat clumsy, is still the best container so far developed for this purpose, although Earle's "modified whiskey flask" bids fair eventually to supplant it. Cultures in either of these flasks can be made directly on the glass without coating of any kind, or on a plasma clot, or on or under cellophane. In preparing the first type, tissue fragments should be placed in the flask with just enough fluid to keep them from drying up; the fluid transferred with the inoculum itself will usually suffice. They are allowed to stand for about a half hour to permit the cells to attach themselves to the glass and culture fluid is then added carefully so as not to wash the implanted tissues loose. They can then be placed in the incubator and within 48 hours will be firmly attached.

The preparation of plasma cultures is very well discussed by Parker (1950) and the reader is referred to his book. Briefly, about 0.5 ml. of chick plasma and 0.5 ml. of embryo extract are pipetted into the flask (a one-ml. hypodermic syringe is better than a pipette) and spread over the entire bottom. From one to three pieces of tissue are then quickly inoculated and placed where they are desired. The plasma will clot within a few minutes and an additional 1.0 ml. of fluid nutrient can then be added on top of the clot. In washing cultures it is this last 1.0 ml. which is removed and replaced. In making subcultures the entire clot is freed from the glass, using a platinum spatula. The clot is rolled and slid out onto a sterile glass plate, the culture is cut out and finally divided into two or four pieces with a sharp knife, and these pieces transferred to fresh clots as inocula.

This method of cultivation on a clot is now rapidly being superseded by the use of perforated cellophane, devised by Evans and Earle (1947). In this method disks of cellophane [2] are cut to a diameter slightly larger than the bottom of a flask. The cellophane must be thoroughly cleaned before use since, as sold, it is coated with a waxy plasticizer. Parker recommends prolonged reflux extraction in hot acetone in a Soxhlet extractor (1950). We have found this helpful but not sufficient. In practice we reflux overnight in acetone. The extractor is then opened and the disks of cellophane (100–200 at a time) are removed and passed through two changes, 10 minutes each, of ether, absolute alcohol, and finally distilled water. They are then placed in the flasks with one ml. of distilled water per flask, and the flasks are stoppered with cotton, and autoclaved. The water is then discarded and the cotton plugs replaced with rubber stoppers. In setting up cultures the nutrient is pipetted into the flasks before inoculating them with tissue. The tissue to be used is washed in Tyrode, Gey, Earle, or White salt-dextrose solution by transferring two or more times to fresh dishes of solution and finally to a dry watch glass. It is then cut up.

While Earle (1939) and others recommend the use of rather large inocula, 2 by 5 mm. on a side, we prefer to cut the tissue quite fine, preferably into pieces not exceeding 0.1 mm. in diameter. The resulting brei is then taken up in a straight pipette and inoculated under the cellophane. If larger pieces are used, they should be transferred with a platinum spatula. After inoculation the cellophane is pushed down with the pipette or spatula to spread the inoculum, after which the flasks, stoppered with No. 0 stoppers, are

[2] Obtainable from Microbiological Associates, Bethesda, Md.

ready for the incubators. Growth occurs largely between the cellophane and the glass, although some cells will pass through the perforations and grow on top. In a classic serum-embryo-extract nutrient, growth from a primary inoculum of

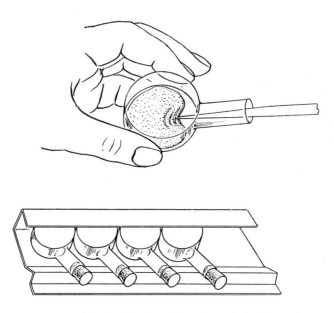

FIGURE 26. Carrel flasks, showing (above) method of inoculating with tissue fragments placed under a sheet of perforated cellophane. Below, four flasks in a rack ready for the incubator.

embryonic tissue should cover the bottom of the flask in about 3–4 weeks.

In making subcultures from such a flask a curved pipette is used. The cellophane is lifted and both glass and cellophane scraped thoroughly with the end of the pipette to loosen the cells. A uniform suspension can be obtained by drawing the fluid into the pipette and ejecting it several times. Earle obtains a still more uniform suspension by pass-

ing through a series of stainless steel wire screens of pro-
gressively finer mesh (Evans, Earle, Sanford, Shannon, and
Waltz, 1951), but this is unnecessary for most purposes.
When thoroughly mixed, the entire suspension is taken up
and distributed in approximately equal parts to a series of
fresh flasks. These may be two, three, up to ten in number,
depending on the density of the original colony. Care must
be taken not to use too small an inoculum in subculturing,
for there is a minimum density below which cultures do not
grow satisfactorily.

Earle's "L" strain of mouse sarcoma cells (derived from
a single-cell isolation—Sanford, Earle, and Likely, 1948—
which is becoming a standard of comparison in many laboratories), Gey's "14 pf" normal rat fibroblasts (Ehrmann and
Gey, 1953), and certain other strains will grow very satisfactorily in flasks or roller tubes without plasma or cellophane. The same principles can be used in handling these
strains. A ten-day Carrel flask culture of "L" strain cells,
for example, is opened and the floor scraped thoroughly. The
contents are then drawn into a one-ml. pipette (about 0.9 ml.
can be drawn off) and distributed in 0.1-ml. aliquots to nine
new flasks, each previously charged with 1.0 ml. of serum-
embryo-extract nutrient.

What has been described is the usual procedure for D-3.5
Carrel flasks. The same applies for Porter flasks (1947), for
Earle's larger Carrel flasks, and for his newer elongated hexagonal flasks, some of which have a floor area of more than
100 sq. cm. and require 20 or more ml. of nutrient. (D-3.5 =
9.6 sq. cm. floor area.)

The plasma method has, it seems to the author, only a
single advantage. Cultures grow radially outward from the
implant at a rate which is relatively uniform on all sides and
in which the margin of the culture is fairly clearly defined.
This permits estimation of growth rates by means of planimetric measurements with considerable precision (see Ebel-

ing, 1921a). This cannot be done with the scattered and loosely distributed growth which occurs directly on glass or under cellophane. On the other hand, growth under cellophane, except with cell strains which make a great deal of collagen, can be estimated fairly accurately by density measurements (light transmission) or by cell counts. And this method has the great advantage of permitting exact control and definition of the nutrient, neither of which can be done in a plasma clot. Porter (1947) has devised a flask in which the end of a 16 by 150-mm. test tube is blown into a flattened bulb similar to a Carrel flask. This is essentially a Carrel flask with a long neck of rather wide diameter, and while it is less subject to contamination than the older type and may be somewhat more easily handled owing to the greater diameter of the neck, its advantages do not seem to be sufficiently greater than standard flasks or roller tubes to make its wide use probable.

Other types of flasks have been devised. Only one, that of Shaw, Kingsland, and Brues (1940), need be mentioned. These authors bored holes in the sides of small flat medicine bottles and sealed thin cover glasses over the holes. Cultures were made on these cover glasses. This permits microscopic examination in an otherwise inexpensive flask which is far less fragile than the Carrel flask. The cover slip, with its culture, can also be removed, stained, and mounted for permanent preservation of the culture. But the finished flask is rather costly and even more clumsy to manipulate than the Carrel flask.

Plant cultures have also been grown in flasks on an agar substratum. Riker and Gutsche have used 6-ounce flat medicine bottles (Blake bottles) charged with 20 ml. of agar. These have been very satisfactory. However, no method has yet been devised by which such plant cultures can be studied *in situ* microscopically.

Tube Cultures

Plant cultures have been largely maintained in 25 by 150-mm. test tubes charged with 15 ml. of agar nutrient, stored either vertically (Gautheret's method, 1942a) or sloped (White's method, 1943a). This permits somewhat greater numbers to be maintained in a small space than with flask cultures, and they are much easier to manipulate. Unlike animal cultures, these tubes not only do not need to be hermetically sealed but must not be so sealed for long periods. They have usually been closed with cotton plugs which, especially with sloped tubes where a large surface area of nutrient is exposed, permits rather rapid desiccation of the agar unless cultures are maintained in a room with controlled high humidity. To obviate this, Gautheret caps the tubes with pieces of tin foil over the cotton (1942a). We have tried aluminum foil without cotton plugs with excellent success. Our best results have been obtained by taking 2 by 2-inch pieces of aluminum foil. The cotton plug with which the tube has been autoclaved is discarded, the tube mouth flamed lightly, and the culture inoculated. A square of aluminum is then placed over the mouth, and bent down around the tube tightly. The aluminum can then be flamed again outside. Enough air will circulate under the aluminum to provide adequate respiration. If desired, the foil cap can be fixed to the tube with a bit of cellophane tape. Morel and Wetmore (1951) use vinyl plastic in place of aluminum, sealing with tape. We have tried "Pliofilm" (a paraffin-rubber film) but without complete satisfaction. Tubes may be closed with rubber stoppers for a week or so, but if sealed for longer periods the cultures will suffer serious retardation. Aluminum foil alone has given us our best results.

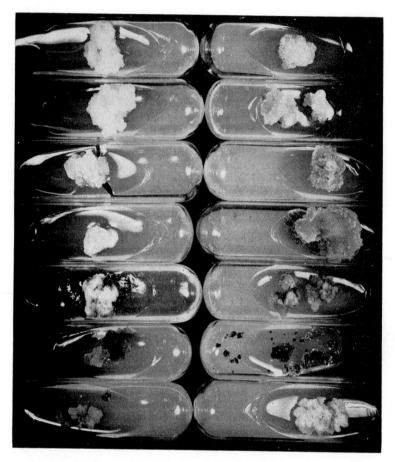

Figure 27. Tube cultures on agar of tissues from 12 different species of plants. Left-hand column, top to bottom: carrot, normal tissue, Gautheret's habituated strain; *Vinca rosea,* tumor tissue from a crown-gall tumor rendered aseptic by heat treatment; *Nicotiana glauca* × *N. Langsdorffii* tumor tissue from a spontaneous, genetically induced sterile tumor, isolated in 1937; another isolation of the same type of spontaneous genetically induced tumor of *Nicotiana;* crown-gall tumor tissue (sterile) of *Nicotiana tabacum,* isolated by Gautheret; sterile tumor tissue from a primary tumor of *Helianthus annuus,* isolated by deRopp; sterile secondary tumor tissue from the Paris Daisy, *Chrysanthemum frutescens,* isolated by Riker; normal tissue of *Scorzonera hispanica,* habituated strain, isolated by Gautheret; normal tissue of *Parthenocissus tricuspidatus;* normal tissue of Virginia creeper, *Par-*

Cultures of plant callus, or of tumors, are placed on top of an agar substratum as a means of exposing them to the air (White, 1939b). While agar is non-nutritive it is not physicochemically inert, introducing as it does adsorptive factors and other elements which cannot be easily estimated. To obviate this objectionable factor Heller and Gautheret have tried replacing the agar with glass wool or glass tape (1947), both of which are unsatisfactory because of the extremely large glass surface exposed to solvent action of the nutrient and introducing thereby factors at least as objectionable as the agar. A better substitute, also devised by Heller (1949), is an inverted cup made by folding a disk of ash-free filter paper over a mandril in the form of a glass tube slightly smaller than the diameter of the culture tube. Once formed, this cup can be slipped into the culture tube in an inverted position and pushed down far enough so that it dips into and remains saturated with the liquid nutrient. The culture can then be placed on this as a support. This is effective only when the tube is kept in a vertical position. For sloped tubes we have folded narrow strips of filter paper, about 5 cm. long and a little wider than the diameter of the culture tube. With the tip immersed in the culture fluid and the culture or cultures placed on the upper part, this has proved very satisfactory (unpublished).

These plant cultures have two important differences from animal cultures. Plant cultures have their optimal pH at about 5.4, which is essentially the point at which an unbuffered aqueous solution is at equilibrium with the CO_2

---

thenocissus quinquifolius; sterile crown-gall tissue of grape, Vitis vinifera; normal tissue of a cactus, Opuntia microacantha (the last four isolated by Morel); gametophytic tissue of Pteridium aquilinum, a fern, isolated by Morel and Wetmore; normal tissue of willow, Salix capraea, isolated by Gautheret. All these, with the exception of the last three, are grown on White's (1943) medium. Opuntia, Pteridium, and Salix require additional vitamins. Two-month-old cultures from explants about 2–3 mm. in diameter.

of the air. They therefore need not be sealed. The optimum
pH for animal tissues, on the other hand, is between 7.2
and 7.6. This can only be maintained by use of powerful
buffer solutions, particularly of solutions containing sodium

A

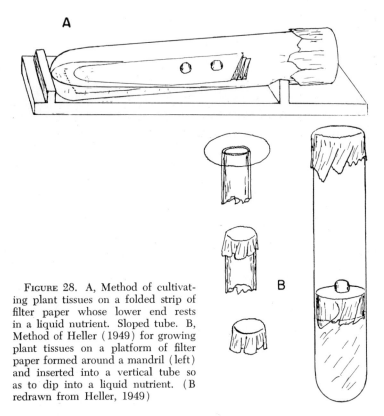

FIGURE 28. A, Method of cultivating plant tissues on a folded strip of
filter paper whose lower end rests
in a liquid nutrient. Sloped tube. B,
Method of Heller (1949) for growing
plant tissues on a platform of filter
paper formed around a mandril (left)
and inserted into a vertical tube so
as to dip into a liquid nutrient. (B
redrawn from Heller, 1949)

B

bicarbonate. But if such a solution is left unsealed it rapidly
loses CO_2 and becomes more alkaline, which is as injurious
to animal tissues as it is to plant tissues. Animal cultures
must therefore be sealed. Further, while no method has yet
been devised for persuading plant cultures to restrict their
growth to the immediate surface of a solid or semi-solid
substratum, which would be a great advantage in micro-

scopic observation, such a habit is, or has at least been considered, a necessary feature of animal cell growth. Animal cells will ordinarily not divide unless they are attached to a substratum. Gey, however, finds evidence (unpublished) that this is not always true. In an undisturbed flask (e.g., Carrel flask) they grow on the bottom of the flask. In order

FIGURE 29. Roller-tube drum for animal or plant cultures. This drum holds 240 16 by 150-mm. tubes, rotating them at a rate of about once in 10 minutes so that the nutrient is constantly circulated.

to obtain adequate oxygenation the covering fluid layer must be very thin, never more than 2 mm. These two facts preclude the use of simple, unsealed, fixed tubes for any animal cell cultures except the virus cultures mentioned before. Yet tubes have certain advantages, especially as regards cost, ease of handling (especially cleaning), and space requirements, over all the various types of flasks so far devised. This has led to the introduction of the roller-tube method, suggested by a number of workers, particularly Carrel (1913c) and Löwenstadt (1925) but first made practical by Gey (1933) and Lewis (1934).

The roller-tube method, in its simplest form, makes use of a standard 16 by 150-mm. test tube. Cultures may be placed directly on the glass, usually four or five per tube, allowing them to stand as described for Carrel flasks, to permit the cells to become fixed to the glass before introducing the nutrient; or the tube may be lined with a thin plasma clot and the cultures implanted thereon; or the cultures may be inserted under a roll of cellophane. The basic principle is the same as for flask cultures. After the cultures are properly in place each tube is charged with either 1.0 or 2.0 ml. of nutrient (the choice is a matter of personal preference; the author uses 1.0 ml.) and closed with a No. 0 stopper. The tubes are then placed in a drum (Fig. 29), which is so sloped as to permit the liquid to cover the lower side of the tube to about half its height from the tip, and is slowly rotated. By this means the cultures are immersed in nutrient for about one minute out of every ten and exposed to the air of the tube for the remaining nine minutes. This provides excellent circulation of nutrient, aeration, and removal of waste products. Nutrient can be removed at 48- or 72-hour intervals and replaced. Cultures grow very well in these tubes. Such tubes cost about 10 cents apiece instead of the $2.25 minimal price of Carrel flasks, are easy to handle and to clean, and occupy little space. They will permit routine examination with a 16-mm. objective, but not higher powers unless special thin tubes are selected or special objectives with a long working distance (2 mm. minimum) are employed. The only costly feature is the rotor. A very good one can be built for about $150, capable of carrying 200 tubes. Much cheaper and simpler ones can be built but will be less sturdy and serviceable.

These tube cultures have had, in common with flask cultures, one serious disadvantage as compared to hanging-drop cultures, namely, that cultures can neither be stained *in situ* for permanent preservation without sacrificing the entire container nor can they be easily removed without injury for remounting. Brues' pierced flask was an attempt to obviate this disadvantage. A partial solution has also been devised by introducing narrow strips of cover glass into the flask or into either round (Pomerat, 1952) or hexagonal (Waymouth, 1950) roller tubes, permitting cultures to grow on these strips and then removing them for permanent preservation. Perforated cellophane seems theoretically to be a better answer to this difficulty since it can easily be removed, fixed and stained, cut into any size desired, and mounted with all the ease characteristic of cover glasses or celloidin sections. In practice, however, it must be attached to the tube with plasma or some similar adhesive since an unattached cellophane "creeps" with the turning of the tube and tears the cells loose faster than they can be attached. Roller tubes can be used for plant cultures, as well as animal cultures, with some advantages, since they offer another means of eliminating the objectionable adsorptive characteristics of agar (White, 1953b).

Other Methods

Most of the cell culture work the world over has been carried out by some one or more of the three methods described above. There are, however, other methods. Of real importance, especially for the study of morphogenesis in massive cultures and for the cultivation of organ primordia, is the watch-glass method variously developed by Fell, Gaillard, Martinovitch, and others. Fell uses a standard chemical watch glass about 5 cm. in diameter set in a Petri dish provided with a ring of moistened cotton, which serves both to support the watch glass and to maintain the required humidity (Fell and Robison, 1929). A plasma clot is prepared in the hollow of the watch glass and the organ to be investigated (limb-primordium, patella, frontal bone, eye,

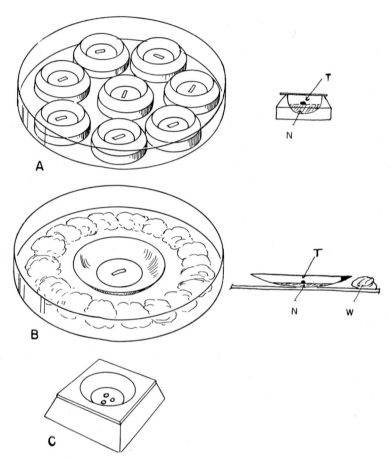

FIGURE 30. Watch glass culture methods. A, Eight U. S. Bureau of Plant Industry miniature Syracuse watch glasses in a Petri dish. The dishes can be individually sealed with one-inch round cover glasses. *T*, tissue; *N*, nutrient. B, Fell's (1928) method using a single chemical watch glass in a Petri dish with cotton (*W*) moistened so that the cultures may not dry out. C, Embryological watch glass as used by Gaillard (1948) and Martinovitch (1950).

etc.) is placed on the surface of the clot. The Petri dish is closed for incubation but may be opened for observation or manipulation of the culture. Manually this is of course far more accessible than any flask or tube. Gaillard (1948) and Martinovitch (1938, 1950) have substituted standard deep-moulded embryological watch glasses (square "salt cellar" type), each covered with its own square cover glass, for similar cultures of glands such as thyroids and ovaries.

It would seem that the small Syracuse watch glass made for the United States Department of Agriculture for the cultivation of nematodes might be superior in some ways to either. These are of such a size that eight of them will fit nicely into a standard 100-mm. Petri dish. Each watch glass can be covered individually with a 25-mm. round No. 2 cover glass, which makes an individual moist chamber of each dish. These covers can be easily removed for manipulation yet can be left on for general observation. The author's laboratory has used such watch glasses for cultures of sporelings of algae (Davidson, 1950), hydroids, amphibian eggs and embryos, fish eggs and embryos, Entomostracae, and for certain types of plant tissue cultures. They are worth more extensive trials. The chief objections to watch-glass cultures are the difficulty in sealing the container to prevent loss of CO_2 and the consequent rise in pH (which forces one to use nutrients of a low bicarbonate content), and the impossibility of making microscopic examination except under the dissecting binocular with a magnification of about 100 diameters. On the other hand, it is an ideal method for making various kinds of chemical studies.

Chapter 7

SETTING UP CULTURES

H AVING organized and equipped the laboratory, prepared the nutrients, and chosen the type of culture and the tissue to be used, we are ready to proceed to the actual setting up of cultures.

Animal Tissues

The chick embryo is the classic example, and will be universally available. Let us assume, therefore, that we are going to prepare three parallel sets of cultures, of chick embryo heart, lung, and leg muscle, in Carrel flasks and roller tubes, in the classic plasma-type nutrient and in a synthetic nutrient of the White or Parker type. We will need:

1 dozen eggs, incubated large end up for 10 days. If so incubated, without turning, the embryo will lie under or near the air sac.

2 half Petri dishes, 10 cm. diameter. These need not be sterile.

2 50-ml. beakers.

6 small Petri dishes, 6 cm., sterile. These can be sterilized in a small tin can (a fruit-juice can is about right), covered with paper or aluminum foil. Dry sterilization, 4 hrs. at 140°C.

1 instrument sterilizer. A one-liter stainless steel beaker with electric heater serves very well. In this is suspended a 50-ml. Pyrex beaker, hung on a stainless steel wire loop.

Fill with distilled water for boiling; the use of tap water results in deposition of calcareous material on beaker and instruments.

2 pairs medium fine forceps, straight.

2 pairs mosquito forceps, straight.

2 pairs medium fine forceps, curved.

2 pairs mosquito forceps, curved.

2 dissecting needles with right-angle knife-ground tips.

1 stainless steel hook, like a button-hook.

2 cataract knives. (Two Bard-Parker knives, No. 7 handle with No. 1 blades will serve the same purpose.)

2 20-ml. hypodermics, sterile.

1 10-ml. hypodermic, sterile.

2 No. 20 or No. 18 needles, 2-inch, sterile.

1 box 10-ml. pipettes, sterile.

A half dozen inoculating pipettes (straight and curved), sterile.

15 Carrel flasks, with cellophane inserts, plugged with cotton.

15 Carrel flasks, without cellophane inserts, plugged with sterile cotton.

1 can 16 by 150-mm. test tubes (about 30 tubes) sterile.

2 Petri dishes of No. 0 stoppers, sterile (36 stoppers).

1 Petri dish of No. 00 stoppers, sterile (36 stoppers).

2 red rubber bulbs.

6 pairs Columbia watch glasses, sterile.

1 piece of steel rod, ½ by 6 inches.

1 micro burner.

1 dissecting shield.

1 wire instrument rack.

Tubes of salt-dextrose solution, plasma, embryo extract, complete classic nutrient (40% serum, 20% embryo extract, 40% salt solution), and synthetic nutrient.

Alcohol, 70%.

The transfer room table is wiped clean with a damp cloth, the "T" supplementary table set up, the dissecting shield set on the table at an angle so that the "T" is at the principal operator's left, the wire instrument rack under the shield and at the right, and the sterilizer filled with water at the right hand of the operator. The heater is started, and coarser forceps and "button-hook" placed in the inner beaker to boil. When thoroughly sterilized they are removed and set on the wire instrument rack. The six small sterile Petri dishes are placed under the shield, at the back. The assistant, sitting at the opposite side of the "T," places two eggs upright in 50-ml. beakers, each set in a half Petri dish. The top of an egg is wiped with a pledget of cotton soaked in alcohol and the egg is cracked all around just below the top with the piece of steel rod. It is then wiped again with alcohol and passed to the principal operator and a second egg prepared in like fashion. The operator takes the egg in the left hand, under the shield, and with a curved forceps held points forward, plunges the tip into the cracked shell. Then, turning the egg in the left hand and "snipping" the forceps like a pair of scissors, the top of the egg is cut off all around (Fig. 31A).

If the break has been high enough the end of the egg will come off just above the air-sac membrane, leaving the membrane intact. Projecting bits of shell can be chipped off, down to the membrane. The forceps are returned to the boiling water and with a second, fresh pair the membrane is lifted off, exposing the liquid interior and the embryo (Fig. 31B, C). The second forceps is placed in the water and the first, now resterilized, is returned to the rack. With a straight forceps in the left hand and the "button-hook" in the right, the allantoic membrane is lifted enough so that the hook can be inserted under the embryo's neck, the embryo lifted out (Fig. 31D), the adherent membranes pulled free, and the embryo deposited in one of the small Petri dishes (Fig. 31E). The egg is then discarded and a second is operated on in the same way. All embryos can be placed in a single Petri dish until it is full. We find the "button-hook" superior to a curved forceps for lifting

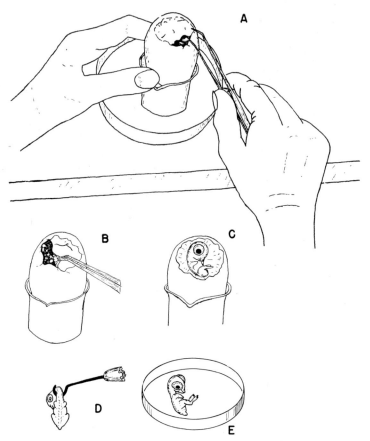

FIGURE 31. Procedures used in preparing chick embryo tissues for cultivation (see text). A, Opening an egg above the air sac, using curved forceps. B, Lifting the air-sac membrane to expose the embryo. C, The embryo, after removal of the air-sac membrane and rupture of the chorio-allantoic membranes. D, Lifting the embryo with a "button-hook" inserted under the neck. It is placed (E) in a small Petri dish, the head removed, and then laid on its back, limbs spread. Holding the embryo with curved mosquito forceps, a midventral incision is made (F). With the outer layers folded back, the viscera (*h*, heart; *p*, lung; *l*, liver; *g*, gizzard) are exposed

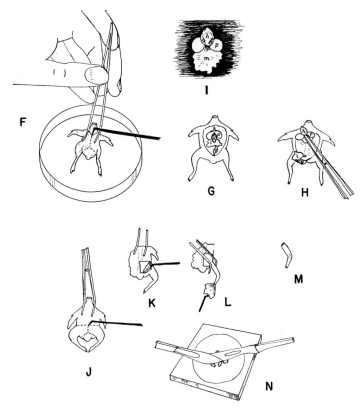

Figure 31. (*Continued*)

(G). The digestive organs are pulled downward, and the heart and lungs carefully separated and pushed forward (H), when they can be transferred to a dish of nutrient (I), mesenteries (*m*) discarded, and heart and lungs placed in separate dishes. The body is then turned over, an incision made down the back (J), the skin pulled down over the leg (K, L), and the leg itself finally removed (M) and transferred to a separate dish of nutrient where the bones can be removed and discarded. Finally all tissues, after washing, are transferred to a dry watch glass and cut up with scalpels (N).

embryos, since there is far less danger of damaging or even severing the neck.

With all the embryos dissected out, three pairs of Columbia watch glasses are opened and placed under the shield. Each is charged with about 1 ml. of salt-dextrose solution. The forceps are exchanged for the finer "mosquito" set and the dissecting needle knives are likewise sterilized. With two small Petri dishes (6 cm.) in front of the operator, the dish of embryos is opened and with a curved forceps the neck of an embryo is severed and the body and head transferred to separate dishes. Then with a curved mosquito forceps in the left hand and a right-angle knife-needle in the right, the body is laid on its back, legs and wings spread. With the points of the forceps laid parallel to the sides of the body, holding it down, a midline incision is made with the needle extending to the upper end of the sternum (Fig. 31F). This is extended as a "Y" to the base of each wing and the body is laid open (Fig. 31G). The needle is then exchanged for a pair of straight forceps. With this the heart is lifted gently forward. The intestines, stomach, and liver are then pulled down between the legs. The lungs are thus exposed and can likewise be lifted forward. Then with the forceps in the right hand, points down and held not quite closed against the base of the heart, the mass consisting of heart, lungs, and diaphragm is pushed forward (Fig. 31H), torn loose from the neck, and laid in the Petri dish (Fig. 31I). The peritoneal membranes are separated and discarded, the heart with the aortic vessels separated from the lungs, and heart and lungs placed in separate watch glasses of nutrient solution. Returning to the Petri dish, the body is then turned belly down and again held with the forceps. With the needle an incision is made down the back, then across above the legs (Fig. 31J). Using the needle as a hook, the skin of the leg can now be everted down to the "heel" joint (Fig. 31K, L). The leg is severed at the "heel" with the knife, then again at the "hip," and the limb, freed of skin (Fig. 31M) is placed in a third watch glass of salt-dextrose solution. The operation is repeated on the other leg, and the carcass is returned to the Petri dish containing the head. This process is repeated until a sufficient number of hearts, lungs, and legs (usually six of each) has been isolated.

Now the covers of the three watch glasses are inverted and filled with nutrient. The aortic vessels are torn out of the hearts and discarded and the hearts are transferred to the fresh nutrient. Since they will have continued to beat during this interval, they should be reasonably free of internal blood. This method of transfer to fresh dishes of nutrient has proved a much more effective method of washing away adherent blood than any number of washings by aspiration with a pipette. The lungs are similarly transferred, depending on peristalsis to free them of occluded amniotic fluid (this will not be complete and some washing out of fluid will continue for several days). The bones are carefully dissected out of the legs and discarded, the muscle being transferred to fresh fluid. This being completed, a third set of watch glasses is prepared but without fluid. The tissues—hearts, lungs, and leg muscles—are transferred with the forceps to these dry dishes, the adherent moisture being sufficient to keep them from drying out.

Before this last operation the cataract knives or Bard-Parker knives have been placed in the boiling water, sterilized, and set on the wire rack to cool. With a knife in each hand, held together like the blades of a pair of scissors (Fig. 31N), the three sets of tissues are now cut up. We prefer to cut them quite fine, so that no fragments larger than about 0.3 mm. remain, while Earle uses strips which, when taken from adult tissue, may be 1 by 3 by 10 mm.

While this is being done the assistant has set out and numbered the Carrel flasks. The desired nutrient is pipetted into those flasks carrying cellophane disks, 1.0 ml. per flask.

For this we use a standard 10-ml. graduated pipette. A 5-ml. syringe is now filled with plasma, either fresh fowl plasma or reconstituted lyophilized plasma and 0.5 ml. is added to each of those flasks lacking cellophane. Then a straight inoculating pipette is chosen, the wide end flamed briefly to remove any loose threads of cotton, and a rubber bulb moistened with boiling water is slipped on. We prefer Becton-Dickinson one-ml. red rubber bulbs to the softer medicine dropper bulb, although the opening in the B-D bulb may have to be enlarged with a rattail file. Some workers prefer to use a blood pipette mouth tube. With the pipette, bits of heart, lung, and leg muscle are placed in the fluid plasma and under the cellophane respectively (see Fig. 26 and accompanying text). Only enough tissue should be taken up each time for a single flask, since greater amounts apparently suffer from crushing and perhaps anoxia. As each cellophane flask is charged, the mouth is flamed and closed with a No. 00 (West S-43) stopper. These cultures are now ready for the incubator. To the flasks containing plasma must be added 0.5 ml. embryo extract, or thrombin, 20 units per ml. (a single drop from a 1-ml. hypodermic with No. 20 needle will suffice). The flasks are shaken enough to mix plasma and embryo extract—if carefully done this can be accomplished without moving the tissue implant too much— or the contents are stirred quickly with a platinum spatula. The flasks are then set aside to permit the plasma to clot. When sufficiently clotted, 1 ml. of the desired nutrient can be added.

We may now turn to the roller tubes. To those which are to carry plasma clots a small amount of plasma is streaked along one side of the interior, extending from the lower end up about 7 cm. This is done with a curved pipette (Gey type), being careful to spread the plasma in a thin but fairly wide band not less than 4 mm. in width. Then with a curved inoculating pipette or, if large pieces are used, with a platinum spatula, four or five bits of tissue are placed in a row along this plasma streak. An equal number of tubes without plasma are similarly inoculated and each tube is laid in a sloping rack with the tissue fragments turned down. The cells will thus become attached directly to the glass and will not migrate on the liquid-air interface. When all are

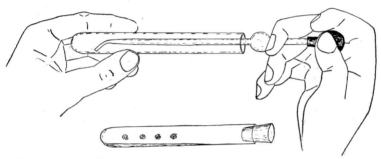

FIGURE 32. Method of inoculating roller tubes. Four (or more) pieces of tissue are placed in a line along the inner surface of the tube. This may be done either with or without a plasma or fibrin clot.

charged, a small amount of embryo extract is added to each plasma tube and mixed quickly with the plasma, using the pipette for this purpose. These tubes are then again laid down horizontally, with the tissue fragments up. They should be allowed to stand for about an hour. Nutrient can then be pipetted into the tubes, 1 ml. per tube, beginning with those without plasma, and proceeding to the others. After charging, the tubes are stoppered with No. 0 (West S-41) stoppers and returned to their racks. They should be left at room temperature for about two hours more before being placed in the rotor incubator. This allows time for cultures without plasma to become attached to the glass. They do not die of desiccation since the atmosphere of the tube is saturated with water vapor and an osmotic exchange goes on constantly between tissue fluids and the fluid nutrient in the bottom of the tube. This osmotic exchange of course supplies no nutrient materials, and if the fluid solution is hypertonic to the tissue it may bring about some "drying," but only to osmotic equilibrium. After the prescribed interval the tubes are transferred to the rotor.

The next task is the preparation of embryo extract. Our small Petri dishes contain 12 embryos, some of which (5 or 6) have been mutilated in excision of tissues for cultivation. A 20-ml. syringe is unwrapped and six embryos picked up with the "button-hook" or forceps and dropped into the barrel. The plunger is inserted. The assistant unwraps two 15-ml. centrifuge tubes and holds them while the principal operator forces the tissue through the syringe into the tubes. We find that six 10-day embryos can be easily handled in such a syringe. No screen, such as recommended by Evans, Earle, *et al.* (1951), Carpenter (1947), and others, is necessary; the mere passing through a 1.0-mm. hole is sufficient to triturate rather thoroughly the embryos, eyes, beaks, bones, and all. To each tube is added an equal volume (estimated visually) of salt-dextrose solution, and the mouths are flamed and stoppered or capped. The same operation is then repeated with the second set of six embryos and a fresh syringe. The brei is thoroughly mixed with a sterile rod and the tubes are set aside in the refrigerator over night. They are then centrifuged at 3000 rpm (1000 × G) for 10 minutes and filtered (see above).

This completes the operations for preparing tissue, inoculating cultures, and preparing embryo extract. All of these operations can be performed by a single worker, without assistants. The operations in which an assistant is most helpful are those involving the simultaneous handling of flasks and stoppers on the one hand and of pipettes and tubes of nutrient on the other, but with adequate racks for flasks and tubes even these can be done alone.

With slight modifications these procedures can be adapted for any tissue. In preparing mouse embryos we choose a gravid female of about 18–20-day gestation. The mouse is killed by pinching the neck with the thumb and forefinger, which separates the vertebrae (Fig. 33A), (an anesthetic is not desirable in such cases) and is pinned out on a piece of cork or pine board covered with white paper and wet with alcohol. These operations are all carried out under the dissecting hood. The belly is swabbed with alcohol and opened with sharp scissors, pinning back the skin, underlying muscle, and peritoneum (Fig. 33B). The lower end of the uterus is grasped with forceps and raised, snipping the uterus and the attached muscles, until the entire uterus can be lifted out and placed in a Petri dish (Fig. 33C). The carcass is discarded. The uterus is then grasped with forceps, snipped with scissors between the embryos, and these are lifted out, pulled away from the placentas, and transferred to a second Petri dish. They are then removed one by one to a Columbia watch glass containing a half ml. of salt-dextrose solution or nutrient, and their thoraxes opened to remove the hearts or other organs (Fig. 33D). Skin taken from the back of such an embryo in sheets 3 to 15 mm. on a side makes excellent material for epithelial cultures. The tissues can then be treated exactly like those of the chick. New-born or day-old mice also make good material. They can be killed by pinching the neck with a forceps. The surface is sterilized by dipping the entire body in 70 per cent alcohol for about a minute and the carcass is then pinned out on a board, opened without further sterilization, and the heart removed. Thoracic muscles and diaphragms from such mice also make good cultures (Fig. 33E).

Adult tissues require somewhat more complex treatment. They must either be removed with the utmost sterile precautions or else, as is the case with most malignant or diseased tissues, they must be treated with antibiotics. A com-

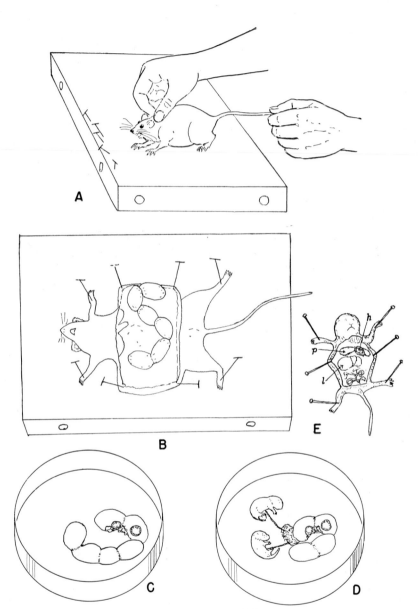

FIGURE 33. Obtaining embryonic material from a mouse. A pregnant female is killed by pinching the neck (A). It is then pinned out on a board, opened by a median and two transverse incisions and the body wall pinned back, exposing the uterus (B). In the case shown there were four embryos in the left-hand horn, two in the right. The uterus is lifted out, cutting away the supporting mesenteries, and is transferred to a sterile Petri dish (C). Here the membrane is opened and the embryos removed (D), and transferred to a second dish for further dissection. In E one of these embryos has been pinned down and opened, exposing the heart (h), lung (p), liver (l), and other organs from which tissue can be taken for cultivation.

134

bination of 10–20 ppm. aureomycin with 0.5 per cent sulfa-
diazine for 24 hours will usually result in the recovery of
sterile cultures from any but the most contaminated tissues.
If this does not suffice, these antibiotics may have to be
incorporated more or less permanently into the nutrient.
Chloromycetin and penicillin are also good, provided they
do not contain toxic impurities. The use of antibiotics is
standard practice in much pathological diagnostic tissue-
culture work but is of course not acceptable in nutritional
studies.

It is worth emphasizing that this entire process involves
no special or expensive equipment except where Carrel flasks
are preferred. In spite of the strictures sometimes laid
against boiling instruments we sterilize our instruments in
this way, merely keeping two or more sets to be used in
rotation so that no instrument is used for two consecutive
operations without immersion in boiling water. We have
never had any difficulties which seemed traceable to this
practice. We use no masks, special gowns, or table covers,
nor do we practice special "scrubbing up" beyond ordinary
cleanliness. Although we restrict movement within the operating room as much as possible, we lay no ban on ordinary
talking. We do not flame instruments, although the mouths
of all tubes and flasks, and all stoppers are flamed. The use
of an operating shield on the table, and ordinary cleanliness,
together with rapidity and precision of manipulation, result
in culture after culture free from contamination. We lose
many cultures from defective nutrients because that is in the
nature of our nutritional studies, and we lose some from
injury in changing nutrients but very few from bacterial
contamination.

One other consideration, I think, belongs at this point.
That is the renewal of nutrient. With any culture which is
growing rapidly, the nutrient must be changed two or three
times a week if required elements, such as dextrose, are to

be kept at a satisfactory level and catabolic products removed. If cultures are kept at lower temperatures, or in an
all-serum nutrient, or if their rate of growth is reduced in
other ways (compare Hanks' surviving cultures for the study
of leprosy, 1947), it may be possible or even desirable to
renew nutrient at much less frequent intervals (Hanks,
1948). The usual practice (see Parker, 1950; Cameron, 1950;
and others) is to suck off the old nutrient with a pipette,
replace it with a wash fluid, usually Ringer's solution, then
after standing for a time aspirate this with a second pipette,
and add fresh nutrient. Where it is necessary to change
nutrient with as little disturbance of cultures as possible,
as with poorly attached fragments; or where loss of suspended
cells would seriously deplete the culture, so that the tubes or
flasks must first be centrifuged or allowed to settle before
removing the supernatant fluid, the removal of the fluid by
pipette is of course necessary. Nevertheless it is our belief
that the introduction of pipettes into the culture tube or
flask is a real source of danger. We have developed a simpler
practice which for most cultures has proved quite successful.

A wire or wooden rack is provided on which the tube or
flask can be inverted so that its mouth rests on the floor of
the rack. A strip of sterile filter paper is placed on this floor
and a second strip is laid on the table in front of the rack.
A series of tubes or flasks are taken one by one, their
stoppered mouths briefly flamed (not enough to scorch the
rubber), then quickly opened, flamed again, and the stopper
set small end down on the strip of paper on the table. The
fluid is poured out into a waste beaker and the tube set up
on the rack so that it drains onto the strip of paper. It is
important that the glass rest directly on the paper so that
capillarity will draw off any fluid which has reached the
mouth. Thus no fluid runs back to carry contaminations into
the tube. After draining thoroughly the tube is taken up,

flamed, fresh nutrient pipetted in, flamed again, and the stopper (likewise briefly flamed) is reinserted. In practice we prefer not to wash the cultures in an intermediate Ringer solution, but if this is desired it can be added in the same

FIGURE 34. A method for draining roller tubes in the process of changing nutrient. The tubes are opened and the stoppers after light flaming are set, small end down, on a strip of sterile absorbent paper. The mouths are flamed, the nutrient poured out, and the tubes stood upright against the back of the rack so as to drain onto a second strip of sterile paper. When thoroughly drained they are again flamed, charged with fresh nutrient, and the stoppers replaced. This method has proved quite satisfactory. It can also be applied to Carrel flasks by using a somewhat differently designed rack.

way. Although this method occasionally washes away cultures which are not well attached to the glass, and also introduces some danger of oxidation products resulting from the flaming of any nutrient residues which may still cling to the mouth of the tube being washed back in any moisture subsequently condensing on the glass, it has seldom resulted in bacterial contamination and is certainly much simpler and more rapid than the older methods. We have seen no reason to alter this method.

One other type of animal culture must be mentioned since it involves special procedures. That is the culture of macrophages or lymphocytes.[1] A 10-ml. hypodermic is filled to 8.4 ml. with a 35 per cent solution of bovine albumin (Armour's crystalline albumin in sterile distilled water) and 1.6 ml. of salt-dextrose solution (Earle, White, or others) is added. Five ml. are then ejected into each of two 15-ml. centrifuge tubes. Ten ml. of fresh heparinized blood (chick, human, etc.) is taken up in a second hypodermic and 5 ml. carefully layered onto the albumin. The tubes are stoppered and centrifuged at 2000 rpm (600 × G) for 10 minutes. At this time the leucocyte layer should be floating at the serum-albumin interface, well above the red blood cells. A narrow pipette is introduced through the supernatant fluid and the leucocyte layer aspirated with about 1 ml. of fluid, being careful not to draw up erythrocytes. The material from two tubes is combined and resuspended in 10 ml. of 10 per cent chicken serum in salt-dextrose solution. This is centrifuged at slow speed for 5 minutes to wash out any remaining plasma or albumin. The supernatant containing the leucocytes is removed and 10 ml. of nutrient medium added. This is then pipetted into Carrel or Porter flasks without cellophane or plasma, 0.5 ml. per flask. The monocytes will be attached to the glass within 24 hours. A sharp shake of the flask will then dislodge all other cell types. The nutrient containing these loose cells can then be removed and fresh nutrient added. Such a culture should cover the bottom of the flask in about 72 hours. It may require the addition of 1–2 drops of 1.4 per cent bicarbonate solution each day to maintain the proper pH (see Fawcett and Vallee, 1952).

[1] Permission to present this method is gratefully acknowledged to Dr. John Hanks (1952).

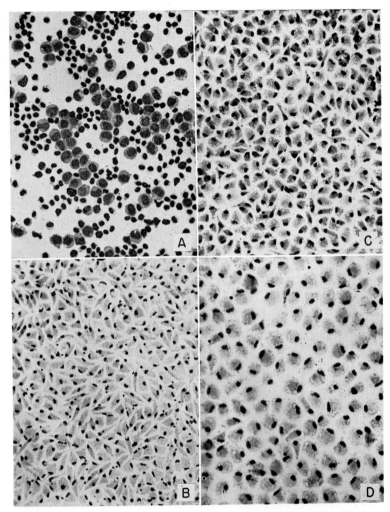

FIGURE 35. Cultures of chick leucocytes isolated by Fawcett's albumin flotation method and grown in Carrel flasks without plasma. A, A fresh smear consisting of monocytes, lymphocytes, and thrombocytes. B, A four-day culture of almost pure monocytes with a few small degenerating thrombocytes (small pycnotic nuclei). C, A culture of the same age, but the cells are larger, resembling both monocytes and macrophages. D, Another four-day culture, in this case consisting entirely of macrophage-like cells. A, ×150 (from Weiss and Fawcett, 1953), B, C, D, ×90. (Courtesy of Don W. Fawcett)

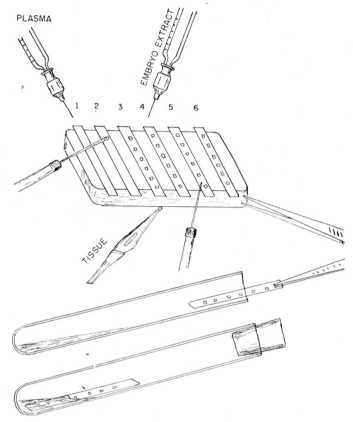

Figure 36. Preparing cultures on narrow cover-glass strips for insertion in roller tubes or Porter flasks. Six strips are laid out on a large culture slide. Plasma is added to each from a pipette or syringe (1), and is then spread evenly with a cataract knife or platinum spatula (2). A series of bits of tissue—skin, for example—are then added in a single row (3) and embryo extract added at each fragment from a second syringe (4). The embryo extract and plasma are quickly mixed with a needle or knife (5) and allowed to clot. The strips are then taken up (6) and slipped into tubes or flasks where they will be bathed in nutrient. They can be inserted singly or they can be placed back to back in pairs, which prevents growth of cells on the backed faces. Cells will quickly grow out over the exposed surfaces of such strips, which can be removed at will for fixation, staining, and mounting. Such mounts are suitable for study at much higher magnifications than can be used with cultures grown directly on the walls of roller tubes.

Cultures of lung, spinal cord, spleen, and other tissues can be prepared much as has been described for heart and muscle. Pomerat (1951) has presented excellent illustrations of setting up spinal cord cultures in his article in *Methods of Medical Research.*

Obviously what has been said applies equally to setting up hanging-drop cultures and cultures on glass or plastic inserts to be placed in the roller tubes. This last method, using cover slips 5 by 40 mm. coated with a thin plasma clot with five or six cultures per strip, and with two such strips laid back to back, held together by capillarity, have been particularly successful in the hands of Pomerat and his group.

Plant Cultures

Let us turn now to the setting up of cultures of plant materials. The first to be grown successfully and still in many ways the most versatile plant material for "tissue culture" is the root tip. These are made available in two ways, from seedlings and from cuttings. First one must have aseptic roots. With many plants having fleshy fruits or membranous capsules (tomato, squash, tobacco, pea, etc.) it is possible to obtain aseptic seeds without chemical treatment of any sort by merely washing the fruit thoroughly and then tearing it open in such a way that the seeds do not touch any surfaces which might be contaminated (White, 1934a). In all cases such tearing, without disinfection, will be the preferred method since it involves no chemical treatment. In other cases, as for example with the grains and small-podded legumes such as alfalfa, this cannot be done and it is necessary to treat the seeds with chemical disinfectants. Bromine water is excellent because of its high volatility, but it is rather difficult to prepare and use. Sodium or calcium hypochlorite, "Dakin solution," mercuric chloride, and the like are more commonly employed. Commercial "Clorox" (sodium hypochlorite) diluted one to six with water makes an excellent substitute for Dakin solution, or it can be prepared by one of the methods outlined by Parker (1950). Antibiotics such as penicillin have shown no advantage over synthetic disinfectants and are not now used for plant material.

One of the most satisfactory methods has been as follows: First the seeds are treated briefly with a wetting agent—alcohol or a detergent. They are then placed in a 1 per cent hypochlorite solution such as "Clorox" or "Pittclor" for periods from 5 to 30 minutes, depending on the species. During this treatment they should be shaken frequently or, better still, treated in a bottle which is rotated slowly on a wheel. The disinfectant is poured off and the seeds washed thoroughly with sterile water. They are then distributed to Petri dishes, either on moist, sterile filter paper or on a layer of 3 per cent agar, and allowed to germinate in the dark. When the roots are 2–3 cm. long all contaminated seedlings are discarded and a selection is made among the rest for vigor and uniformity. The selected tips are severed with a sharp scalpel and inoculated into flasks for cultivation. Seeds may also be placed for germination directly in the culture flasks of nutrient, but a contaminated or non-viable seed then requires discarding the entire flask.

The above procedure is quite satisfactory for most purposes. Occasionally, however, it is for some reason impossible to use seedling roots. A typical example is the case where it is desired to cultivate roots carrying a series of related virus infections (White, 1934b). The inoculation of viruses into roots after their establishment in vitro has not proved feasible. It is therefore necessary to obtain roots which are already infected. For this purpose it is necessary to use adventitious roots developed from infected plants. This can be done in two ways. Stem tissues of many plants such as sunflower, tobacco, tomato, and carrot will produce occasional roots during the first few weeks when cultured *in vitro* on a nutrient containing traces of one of the growth hormones, such as naphthalene-acetic acid (10^{-6}). With these plants one may isolate tissues as if for the preparation of cambial cultures (see below), and when roots appear thereon these can be severed and transferred to fresh flasks. They must, indeed, be so transferred, for roots, although initiated freely in a solution containing a growth substance, will not continue to grow in such a solution for even very brief periods after excision (Nobécourt, 1939). These growth substances are extremely toxic to unattached roots.

While this method involves little risk of secondary contamination, it is uncertain in results. For some purposes it may be better to use cuttings. Stems of tomato, for example, will grow adventitious roots quite easily. Pieces of stem about 20 centimeters long are washed thoroughly with a detergent, then with a disinfectant such as hypochlorite, and finally with sterile water. They are then rigidly attached to a suitable sterilized cork cover and suspended in a jar whose atmosphere is kept saturated from a layer of filter paper resting in the sterile water at the bottom and bent around the inside of the jar. Roots will emerge from such cuttings after a week or ten days, and will in many cases be quite aseptic. They can then be removed for cultivation. The chief hazard here is the possibility of a film of water condensing on the stems, which might spread contaminations. Nevertheless the experimenter may be surprised at how free such stems generally are of infections if kept free of surface moisture (White, 1934b, 1943a).

Once isolated in an aseptic condition, cultures will be maintained as will be described in a later chapter.

The general principles for the isolation of stem growing points are essentially the same as those for root tips, only complicated somewhat by the presence of enclosing leaves or bud scales. These serve as a protection against contamina-

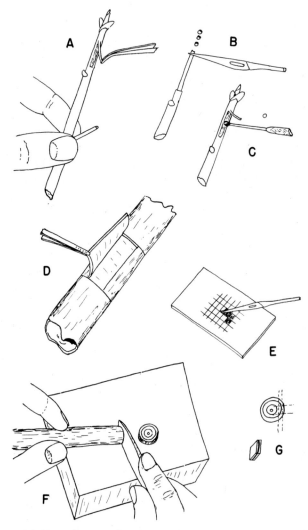

FIGURE 37. Procedures used in setting up cultures from woody tissues of plants. A, A succulent stem such as squash or tomato is stripped of its leaves. The outer layers (epidermis and cortical tissues) are carefully torn forward exposing the procambial region. Transverse cuts are then made (B) with a sterile knife, providing disks of tissue which can be used as primary inocula. Alternatively, cambial tissue can be exposed in a narrower

tion, however, and if removed carefully will leave an aseptic core (White, 1933a). When it becomes a question of isolating cultures from more massive stems and roots, however, somewhat different procedures must be applied. Such tissues will consist of (1) procambium, (2) lateral primary cambia, (3) secondary cambia, and (4) parenchymatous or other tissues which have retained a meristematic character.

1. Procambium. There are two general procedures for isolating tissues from young stem tips, both applicable especially to relatively fleshy stems such as tomato, tobacco, and sunflower. The stem should be cut to a length of 15–20 cm. and the leaf petioles severed close to the stem. Then, beginning 3–5 cm. from the tip, the epidermis and the underlying cortical parenchyma are lifted with a scalpel and torn forward so as to strip off the entire surface. When these tissues, which may be contaminated with molds or bacteria, are eliminated, the now aseptic core is severed with a scalpel. It may then be cut into short disks 0.5–1.5 mm. in thickness, which are transferred to the nutrient medium (Fig. 37A, B). A second method which is often equally successful is to remove the epidermal layers from only one side of the tip. When an aseptic area has been exposed, a well-sharpened surgeons' ear curette of 1.0-mm. diameter is pushed into the soft meristematic tissue and a sharp turn will remove a 1-mm. "melon ball" of tissue (Fig. 37C). This last method is espe-

---

area and sterile tissue removed with a surgeons' ear curette (C). For older, more woody stems, the entire bark is removed (D) and blocks of tissue removed from the phloem by a series of intersecting cuts (E). As a third method the surface of a small woody stem, not more than a centimeter in diameter, can be sterilized by chemical disinfectants, by burning, by scraping, or by a combination of methods. Transverse sections are then made (F) and these are finally cut so as to leave small blocks of tissue traversed by the cambium (G). Such blocks should be implanted in the agar on edge so that the cambium is in contact with the substratum to various depths.

Most of the cultures shown in Fig. 27 were isolated by one of these methods.

cially useful when dealing with young galls or tumors or with plants whose epidermis does not strip well. In such cases the stem may be split some distance back of the tumor or the growing tip, and torn forward. If the tear passes through the desired tissue the curette can be used to remove the specimen. This is essentially equivalent to "punch biopsies" in animals.

2. Cambium. There are likewise two methods for securing specimens of lateral cambia from older plants such as trees. The first, developed especially by Gautheret (1934), is useful principally for isolation during the growing season, April to August in northern climates, while the second method, introduced by Gioelli (1938a, b) but likewise much used by Gautheret (1942a), serves better during the dormant season. If one is dealing with woody stems only a few centimeters in diameter the entire branch should be cut and brought into the laboratory. If it is during the growing season while the cambium is soft, an incision can be made around the stem at two points above and below the region of interest and 2–5 cm. apart, depending on the size of the branch, a longitudinal incision made, and the bark peeled off (Fig. 37D). These incisions need not be aseptic. Then, being careful to touch only the edges of the exposed areas, the bark is flattened on a block of wood so as to expose the inner surface. A series of shallow incisions is then made in such a manner that they intersect in a checkerboard pattern but do not extend to the edge of the piece (Fig. 37E). A very satisfactory pattern is provided with the transverse incisions about 3–5 mm. apart and the longitudinal ones 1–2 mm., but smaller patterns may be used. The incisions should not pass more than half way through the bark. The exposed inner surface is of course aseptic and if the incisions have not extended either deep enough to reach the contaminated outer bark nor far enough laterally to intersect the possibly contaminated marginal primary incisions, a series of similar

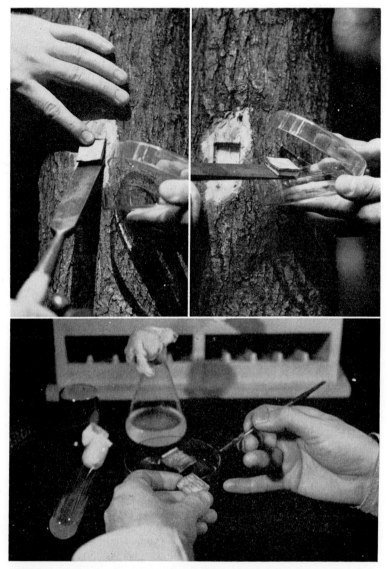

FIGURE 38. Preparing cultures from the cambial region of large trees. A block of wood is cut out by four deep cuts of a chisel and placed in a Petri dish, care being taken that it does not split at the cambium, and bits for inoculation are taken from the phloem side of the tissue thus exposed. (From White, 1943a, Figs. 36 and 37)

aseptic explants can then be lifted out. These are placed in culture tubes on nutrient agar with the cambium face up, or they may be set on edge and pushed into the agar to a depth of about half their width. They should then be oriented in a position opposite to that in the plant so as to take advantage of the normal polar movement of auxin.

The same method can be used for larger stems of trees and other woody plants. Here an area of bark is cleaned with a sharp chisel or draw knife. Then four intersecting incisions are made with chisel or saw, 10–15 cm. apart and passing well into the wood. The enclosed block is lifted out, being careful that it is not split at the cambium, and taken into the laboratory. Here, in a sterile room, the cambium is exposed and the same procedure followed (Fig. 38). Cultures from such blocks are more likely to be successful from the phloem side than from the wood.

The method described above is that introduced by Gautheret. It is most easily applied when the cambium can be exposed, but during the dormant season this is not possible. Small branches or excised blocks may then be brought into the laboratory as before. In the case of branches the surface must be sterilized. An effective method is first to clear them of adherent debris by scrubbing with soap and water. They are then dipped in 95 per cent alcohol and the alcohol burned off several times. This will usually provide reasonable asepsis. The stem is then laid on a sterile block and a series of transverse cuts made, about 1 mm. apart. If the stem is small, 2–5 mm. in diameter, the entire transverse disk may be used as an explant (Fig. 37F). If it is more than 5 mm. in diameter, it may be best to divide the initial disk into sectors and dissect off and discard the outer cortical (bark) tissues and much of the wood. This provides a rectangular block with its long axis tangential to the original surface and traversed by the cambium (Fig. 37G). If this block is pushed into the agar perpendicular to the surface and to a depth such as to leave about half the block exposed, growth will occur from the cambium above the agar surface and will ultimately spread out onto the agar, at which time it can be dissected away from the original block and subcultured.

The same principle can be applied to blocks from larger trunks of trees, but in this case the incision can be done without any disinfection. The block is brought into the laboratory, care being taken not to contaminate the inner surface. The wood (xylem) is dissected away to within about one mm. of the cambium and from this sterile surface a series of strips are separated by deep longitudinal cuts 3 mm. apart. The strips thus formed are cut into blocks by transverse cuts, 1–2 mm. apart and the bark is then removed by tangential cuts and discarded. The blocks left, rectangles 1 by 3 by about 2 mm. in thickness, are used as explants. This method has been successful with wood of elm, oak, beech, willow, pine, spruce, and many other trees as well as with shrubby plants, like rose, and vines such as grape and Virginia creeper, especially in the hands of Morel at Versailles and Wetmore at Harvard.

The same general principles apply to the isolation of secondary cambia or of parenchyma from fleshy organs, such as tubers. An aseptic surface is exposed either by breaking (carrot), tearing, or when necessary by first disinfecting a surface area and then cutting it away (potato, for example). Then with a sterile cork-borer of 2–3 mm. diameter a series of cores are removed and laid in a Petri dish. With a scalpel or a specially designed cutter (Steward and Caplin) a series of transverse cuts are made in these cores, providing a series of comparable disks. This method has been used with tissues of carrot (Caplin), artichoke (Gautheret), and other fleshy plants.

There remains a number of special tissues, only one of which need be discussed in detail. The intercalary meristems of grasses, rushes, and certain vines offer theoretical advantages in being easily isolated with relatively little trauma but have been little studied. The fleshy axillary (stipular) gemmae of *Marattia* and *Lycopodium* should be ideal cryptogamic material comparable in structure to the tubers of phanerogams but have not been studied so far

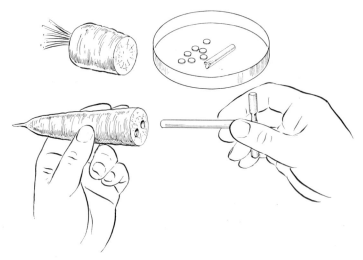

FIGURE 39. A method for preparing cultures from fleshy organs, tubers, and the like. In this case a carrot is represented. The carrot is washed but is not chemically disinfected. It is then broken. With a sterile cork-borer, a series of cores are removed which contain the cambium layer. These cores are cut transversely into disks of uniform diameter and thickness, which are used as primary inocula.

as I know. The most important of these materials is the embryo proper, which has gained great significance in studying the genetics of certain usually "sterile" hybrids, and in shortening the dormant period of grasses. Very young embryos have not been successfully grown, but by the time the cotyledons have been fully initiated, in the early "torpedo" stage, they can usually be excised and grown quite readily. Once this stage has been determined in terms of days after fertilization, the young ovules can be removed. An incision

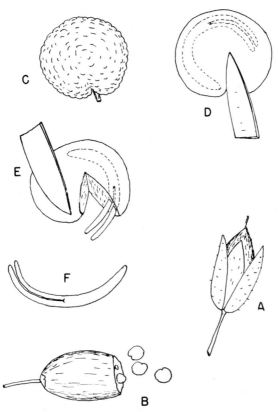

FIGURE 40. Preparation of plant embryos. The common chickweed, *Stellaria media,* is represented. The fruit (A) is about 6 mm. long. This is surface-sterilized and is then opened by a transverse cut and the seeds pressed out (B) onto a sterile glass plate moistened with nutrient solution. The seeds (C), which are about 1 mm. in diameter when ripe, are cut so as to remove a wedge, so placed that it does not intersect the enclosed embryo (D). Then with the flat of the knife, pressure is applied at the micropylar end so that the embryo is forced out (E). These embryos (F) can be used as inocula or the root can be removed for cultivation. The same general method applies to the removal of still younger embryos. (Compare with Fig. 10J.)

at the micropylar end, if not too deep, will expose the embryo uninjured and sharp pressure at the opposite end of the seed will eject the embryo. In the case of monocotyledons the scutellum can be dissected off and the embryo removed. It should then be transferred quickly to the definitive nutrient. In all these cases it is important that the embryo or tissue fragment shall not be allowed to become desiccated, and when implanted that it shall have adequate surface contact with the agar but shall not be covered by too deep a film of liquid.

These, then, are the general methods for the isolation of plant materials for cultivation.

Chapter 8

GROWTH MEASUREMENTS AND THEIR INTERPRETATIONS

THE CHIEF aims of "tissue cultures" are, as we have said, first the setting up of a group of conditions which shall adequately duplicate all the essential features of the environment in which the organ, tissue, or cell lives in nature in such a manner that its behavior therein is qualitatively and quantitatively "normal," that is, similar to what it would have been in its native environment; and second, the study of the quantitative and qualitative changes which take place in the behavior of the cell, tissue, or organ, when single elements of these conditions are altered. This gives us a measure of the importance and function of each characteristic of the environment in the economy of the material under investigation, permits us to sort out the significant from the purely fortuitous elements of behavior, thus simplifying our picture of the real organism, and should lead to a better understanding of behavior itself.

While a qualitative evaluation of resultant changes is an essential part of any set of observations, such evaluations, being largely descriptive, are of necessity subjective in character. They must inevitably fall short of the ideal requirements of complete scientific precision. Science rests on *quantitative* representation, even of changes in *quality*. And quantitation is essentially synonymous with measurement. It is thus natural that measurement should play a dominant role in cell culture studies, and that the accuracy and reliability of measurements should be a major concern of the student of the subject. What, however, are we to measure?

Living organisms (particularly those which, like most plants, are incapable of autonomous movement, or like massive tissues and many tissue cells, are restricted in their movements) react visibly to changes in environment chiefly by changes in character, velocity, and extent of growth. Growth consists of increase either in mass or complexity of one or more parts of the living material or its products. Which of these factors is to be measured will depend on available techniques. Increase in mass may be estimated in terms of linear dimensions, wet or dry weight, cell number, rate of increase in cell number (mitotic index), increase of some vital constituent (such as phosphorus, amino nitrogen, sugar, nucleic acid), or removal of some specific constituent such as phosphorus or sugar from the nutrient, or by some metabolic measure such as respiratory rate. Increase in complexity may be measured by decrease in cell size or change in ratio between total mass and cell number.

Perhaps the simplest of all such methods is that applicable to root cultures. When grown in culture, roots do not undergo secondary thickening. As a result they ordinarily take up within a few millimeters of the growing point a diameter characteristic of the species and of a particular culture medium, and retain this diameter throughout the length of even very old cultures. The cross sectional area is thus a constant and can be ignored in comparing measurements, so that length alone becomes an accurate measure of volume. Fiedler, by parallel measurements and weighings of a series of cultures of different lengths, has verified the fact that length and weight bear a constant relation to one another (Fiedler, 1936). This, of course, takes no account of any branches which may form, but actual study has shown that, within the one-week passage generally used for such cultures, the error so introduced is never more than 10 per cent and seldom more than 3 per cent, and this error is always negative in value (White, 1943a). Day by day measurements can then be made on a single culture, with an ex-

FIGURE 41. Method of measuring roots grown in 125-ml. Erlenmeyer flasks, using a flexible celluloid rule. Measurements can be made with an average error of less than 10 per cent without removing the roots from the flasks. (From White, 1943a, Fig. 40)

perimental error of less than 10 per cent, without disturbing the culture. Growth curves can thus be established and the environmental effects studied with a high degree of both precision and flexibility. Growth itself is usually measured with a flexible celluloid rule, either by bending the rule to approximate the curvature of the root (Fig. 41) or by wash-

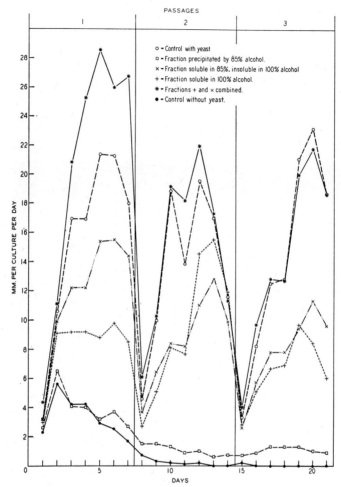

FIGURE 42. Graph showing in *mm./culture/day* the average day-to-day increments over three consecutive passages of seven days each of groups of ten clonally derived tomato roots grown in six nutrient solutions consisting of a standard salt-sucrose solution to which have been added six different fractions or groups of fractions of an extract of dried brewers' yeast. This shows the degree of precision obtainable in using excised roots, grown and measured as shown in Fig. 41, in the study of nutritional problems. (From White, 1937a, Fig. 8)

ing the root up onto the side of the flask where it can be laid out straight (White, 1943a). Roots can, of course, be removed from the culture medium and laid out directly on a sterile rule, but the risk of contamination is so great and the degree of accuracy obtainable without such removal is sufficient so that the more precise method is seldom justified.

Unfortunately no animal tissue is adapted to such simple methods. The nearest approach is that developed by Ebeling (1921a). When animal tissue cultures such as fibroblasts are grown in plasma clots, either in hanging drops or flask cultures, there is a regular increase in colony diameter, with a fairly sharp visible margin. If the image of such a culture is projected and traced at hourly, daily, or weekly intervals, and the area of the consecutive images measured with a planimeter,

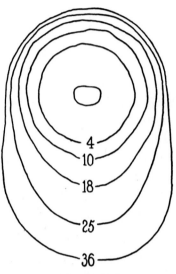

FIGURE 43. Projection tracing showing the increase in area of a strain of skeletal fibroblasts grown in a plasma clot for 36 days. (From Parker, 1932a, Fig. 4)

fairly regular and duplicable growth curves can be plotted (Ebeling, 1921a, b; Parker, 1931, 1932a, b). Similar curves of horizontal area-increase can be constructed for plant callus cultures. It is recognized that this method may err in making no distinction between cell increase and cell migration, and in taking no account of changes in the thickness of the cultures. In cultures of fibroblasts these errors may be unimportant so long as the physical and chemical properties of two nutrients under comparison are not notably dissimilar, but with plant callus cultures certainly, and probably with most animal cells as well, they may be so great as completely to vitiate the result. Even in animal cultures grown under standard conditions, the individual variations among different strains of cultures may be fairly great (Parker, 1931, 1932a, b), and any variation in nutrient composition will introduce physical changes which may alter the migration (spreading) rate without changing the mitotic rate in a comparable direction. This method is therefore not a valid one for physiological studies.

For plant callus cultures, therefore, and for many types of animal cultures, resort must be had to some alternative method. That most used for plant cultures has been weight. Hildebrandt, Riker, and Duggar (1946), and Hildebrandt and Riker (1949, 1953) have taken the average initial weight of a group of explants and then sacrificed all cultures at the end of the experiment. This gives a measures of total increase but provides no growth curve. Caplin and Steward have refined this (1948, 1949) by taking carefully standardized initial explants, setting up large numbers of cultures, and then sacrificing a standard small number of cultures (four, for example) at daily or biweekly intervals to obtain growth curves. Because of the small numbers represented by each point on such a curve, individual variations among cultures may play an important disturbing role.

White has shown that it is quite possible to weigh such cultures at daily or biweekly intervals without destroying them (1953b). The culture is lifted out on a platinum loop, placed on a sheet of sterile filter paper to remove excess moisture, then transferred to a 1 by 1 cm. square of sterile paper on the pan of a precision torsion balance, weighed, and returned to its tube. Under a dissecting shield this can be done aseptically and growth curves can be established for single cultures. Interestingly, such cultures grow much faster than do cultures which, like those of Hildebrandt and

Riker, are left undisturbed (Fig. 44). A similar technique can be used for animal "organ cultures" such as those of Fell (1931) and Gaillard (1948), but is unfortunately not applicable to the more minute animal tissue cultures except

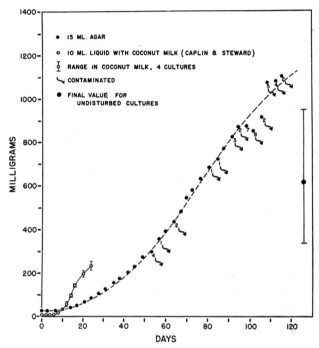

FIGURE 44. Graph showing the increase in weight in milligrams of three groups of cultures derived from carrot root tissues and grown over periods up to 124 days on three types of nutrients. (From White, 1953b)

by pooling many cultures for each weighing (Meier, 1931; Laser, 1933). For these the Cartesian diver technique developed by Danes and Leinfelder (1951) appears to be the only one practicable for single cultures, and this method is so specialized that it is unlikely to come into general use.

All of these direct measurements make no distinction between living material and its non-living products (cellulose, collagen, etc.), nor between growth by increase in mass and growth by increase in complexity, which may involve an actual diminution in mass. Indirect methods must be used to obviate these difficulties. One of these involves the determination of rates of cell division. If the thin areas of a culture are either fixed and stained, or examined by phase-contrast, or by Willmer's photographic method (1933), cells in mitosis can be recognized. If the number of cells in a given mitotic stage, in metaphase for example, is compared with the total number of living cells in a given area, a figure is obtained which, when compared with a corresponding figure for another culture, gives a measure of the relative rates of increase in cell number in the two cultures. While this can be done with fair precision, it must be used with caution. Marginal areas, which are the only ones in which such cells can be observed in a living state, are supposedly in a more active mitotic state than those at the core of a massive culture so that a rapidly migrating, hence widely-spread culture, may falsely seem to be growing more actively than a more compact one. Moreover, cell divisions tend to occur in cycles which may involve time sequences so that indices obtained at different times of day on different cultures cannot safely be compared. Earle has refined this method by making standard inoculations with a suspension of cells, and subsequently making nuclear counts on standard samples drawn from such suspensions (Sanford *et al.*, 1951).

While this seems to be as accurate a measure of increment as are linear measurements or weighings (about 10% ± error), it is applicable only to cells which will grow as suspensions or loose aggregations such as fibroblasts, lymphocytes, and sarcoma cells, and cannot be used for epithelium, nerve cells, bone, muscle, and the like. For these last, some form of metabolic measure seems best. Most of these methods, although not all, require the destruction of the culture, hence the use of large numbers of cultures, to obtain significant results. This is true for determinations of amino nitrogen, nucleic acids, sugars, and for indirect measurements of respiration. Direct-method respiration studies, however, can be made continuous (Barcroft method) and methods of this

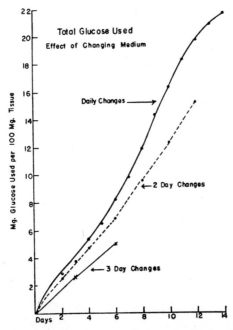

FIGURE 45. Graph showing amounts of glucose utilized, expressed as mg. glucose per 100 mg. tissue per day, by three sets of chick fibroblast cultures under three different experimental conditions. (From Wilson, Jackson, and Brues, 1942, Fig. 1)

sort have been refined, again by Danes and Leinfelder (1951) (Cartesian diver method), so that studies can be made on single cultures. Interestingly enough, these workers, as well as Kirk *et al.*, have shown that a high respiratory rate can be negatively correlated with both mitotic index and migration rate. This and similar methods will certainly be much more widely used in the future.

Finally, as an extension of this last, Brues with animal cells (Wilson, Jackson, and Brues, 1942) has made use of the rate at which certain substances, such as radioactive phosphorus and glucose, disappear from the nutrient. These give excellent measures of metabolic activity and can be carried out without destroying or disturbing the culture itself. They require special methods and equipment, however.

Replications

As anyone who has worked with biological materials is aware, such materials regularly show a considerable degree of variability. This is true even of clonal strains, such as our 20-year-old strain of tomato roots or Carrel's old strain of fibroblasts, although both Parker and Earle seem to have been able to reduce this variability to a relatively low level. Recognizing the reality of this variability, even under well-controlled conditions, it is evident that such materials can seldom be treated as individuals, but must be treated statistically. This being the case, it is important to decide first how many replications are necessary in order that significant results can be obtained and, second, how wide a difference in result must a given experimental variable produce in a series of the chosen number of cultures before that effect can be considered as being due to this variable and not to chance. Decision on the first point involves a compromise between the ideal of a very large number on which to base averages, on the one hand, and on the other hand the number which can be practicably handled in a laboratory with restricted space, facilities, and limited time. In dealing with root cultures this laboratory has chosen twenty as the standard number to be used in establishing averages and each experiment is repeated at least three times. In dealing with callus cultures, not more than ten cultures can be handled successfully in each experimental variant of a large experiment. The testing of two concentrations of three different substances in all possible combinations would involve 27 experimental combinations, hence 540 simultaneous root cultures or 270 callus cultures. It is ordinarily not possible to handle animal materials in such numbers except by the roller-tube method. Even with these numbers a wide spread between experiment and control is usually necessary before results are statistically significant. One example, involving 400 root cultures, is given in the table on the following page.

In this group of experiments, each set of 20 root cultures grown under one set of conditions on a particular date is compared with 20 cultures grown either under a different set of conditions on the same date or else under the same conditions but on different dates. Here differences up to 12 per cent between series (Nos. 1, 2, 3, 4, and 10) are without statistical significance; differences of 24 and 25 per cent (Nos. 5 and 8) are of doubtful significance (odds of less than 20:1 against the results being due to chance) while differences of 31 per cent and over (Nos. 6, 7, and 9) are highly significant (odds of more than 20:1 against the results being due to chance). This analysis indicates that in experiments carried out in this way and using 20 replications in each experimental complex, differences of 30 per cent and over can, in general, be relied on to indicate a true difference in behavior and not merely fortuitous differences due to the variability of the material. Data on animal tissue cultures have usually not been presented in this fashion and it is somewhat doubtful if we are yet ready for their treatment with mathematical and statistical precision except by Sanford *et al.*'s (1951) nuclear count method, and under exceptional conditions by area measurements as has been done recently by Ehrmann and Gey (1953).

Growth of Excised Tomato Roots Cultivated Either Simultaneously or Consecutively in Different Nutrient Solutions, with a Statistical Analysis of the Significance of the Results †

No.	Series I	Series II	Mean total increments in mm. I	Mean total increments in mm. II	Difference I minus II	Diff. = % of I	t*	Odds in favor of difference being significant
1	Yeast June 7–14, 1938	Yeast June 9–16, 1938	77.7 ± 6.1	71.4 ± 6.1	6.4 ± 8.7	8	0.74	nil
2	Yeast June 9–16, 1938	Yeast June 19–26, 1939	71.4 ± 6.1	68.2 ± 6.6	3.2 ± 9.1	4	0.35	"
3	Yeast June 7–14, 1938	Glycine + 10^{-7} B$_1$ June 9–16, 1938	77.7 ± 6.1	79.7 ± 8.8	− 2.0 ±10.7	3	0.19	"
4	Yeast June 7–14, 1938	Glycine + 10^{-7} B$_1$ June 9–16, 1938	71.4 ± 6.1	79.7 ± 8.8	− 8.3 ±10.7	12	0.78	"
5	Yeast Jan. 19–26, 1939	Glycine + 10^{-9} B$_1$ Jan. 19–26, 1939	68.2 ± 6.6	51.6 ± 6.0	16.6 ± 8.6	24	1.93	< 20 : 1
6	Yeast Jan. 19–26, 1939	Glycine + 10^{-10} B$_1$ Jan. 19–26, 1939	68.2 ± 6.6	47.2 ± 4.2	21.0 ± 7.8	31	2.69	> 20 : 1
7	Yeast June 9–16, 1938	10^{-7} B$_1$ June 9–16, 1938	71.4 ± 6.1	34.0 ± 2.5	37.4 ± 6.7	52	5.58	> 100 : 1
8	10^{-7} thiamin (B$_1$) June 9–16, 1938	10^{-7} B$_1$ Jan. 19–26, 1939	34.0 ± 2.5	44.8 ± 3.7	−10.8 ± 4.5	25	2.40	< 20 : 1
9	Glycine + 10^{-7} B$_1$ June 9–16, 1938	10^{-7} B$_1$ June 9–16, 1938	79.7 ± 8.8	34.0 ± 2.5	45.7 ± 9.2	58	4.97	> 100 : 1
10	Glycine + 10^{-7} B$_1$ June 9–16, 1938	Glycine + 10^{-7} B$_1$ Jan. 19–26, 1939	79.7 ± 8.8	82.3 ± 7.7	− 2.6 ±11.2	3	0.23	nil

* t = ratio of mean differences to the standard deviation of the mean difference.

† Table 3, White, 1943a.

Presentation of Results

It is seldom necessary or desirable to present the numerical data of an experiment *in toto*. The results can usually be presented better in the form of graphs. Where average final results for total passages are desired, histograms will be most useful, while curves will be required where temporal trends are important. Where a number of simultaneous experiments are to be compared, the results can be presented in absolute units—mm. (Fig. 46A), or mg., nitrogen percentage, or Q_{O_2}, for example. Where experiments are carried out on different tissues, or under conditions where uncontrolled variables in the environment may have as great or greater effects on growth rates as do the intentionally manipulated experimental variables, expression in absolute units may be meaningless. Since all cultures of one cell type react on the average in approximately the same way and to the same extent to most variables in the environment, uncontrolled as well as controlled, this difficulty can often be obviated by setting up a control in each series, treating this control always as the norm and comparing all other cultures within a series with the control. The percentage results can then be compared from one experiment to another, which could not be done with the absolute values (Fig. 46B). Thus in two series on the effects of vitamin B_6 (pyridoxin), on two different strains of roots using 1.0 ppm. pyridoxin as the only organic accessory substance (in addition to salts and carbohydrate), but carried out on two different dates, the series completed July 13, 1939, gave a *numerical* index of 58.6 mm. while that completed on December 7, 1939, gave an index of only 21.8 mm., but the *percentage* values for the two were 60 and 62 respectively. While the use of percentages may be objected to on the grounds that it involves a subjective choice of standard, it is

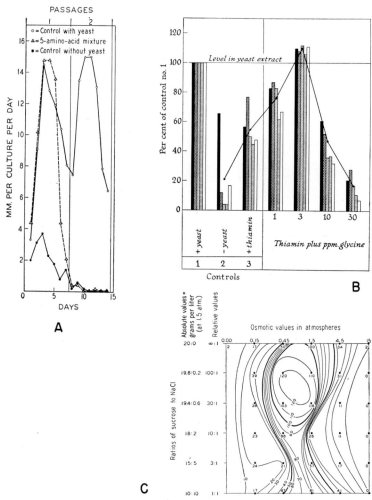

FIGURE 46. Three methods of presenting in graphical form numerical data on the increments of excised tomato roots. A, Line graph representing increments in *mm./culture/day* over two seven-day passages under three sets of experimental conditions. B, Histogram representing increments in terms of percentage of a control over five passages under six sets of experimental conditions. C, Isopleth diagram showing total increments in millimeters of a series of cultures grown in 36 solutions representing the simultaneous variation of two sets of nutrient variables: osmotic value and ratio of sucrose to NaCl concentration. (A from White, 1943a, Fig. 45; B from White, 1939c, Fig. 4; C from White, 1942, Fig. 5)

the only way in which nonsimultaneous experiments can be compared, and has proved very satisfactory as a method of presenting results. Three examples of graphical representation will serve to show the types found most useful (Fig. 46).

Interpretation

While the results themselves should, wherever possible, be presented in numerical form with a definite idea of the degree of accuracy and significance which can be attached to them, the interpretation of results is the duty of the observer. It is necessary for him to take into account not merely the numerical data, but also many qualitative features of the results which cannot be set down in numerical form. Interpretation involves the integration of many sorts of information which only the person who handles the cultures can have available. This is a subjective matter. How it is to be done is entirely personal and cannot be set down in any handbook. Yet it is in this, just as much as in the planning of an experiment and the recording of data, that a scientist shows his true caliber. It does not seem amiss, therefore, to emphasize its importance, as well as its difficulty.

Chapter 9

APPLICATIONS

THE HISTORY of any biological method covers, in general, three phases which may or may not be simultaneous. These are the development and perfection of basic techniques, the application of these techniques to already recognized problems, and the formulation of new and unforeseen applications. Harrison began with the second phase in this series, having before him a definite problem, the elucidation of the origin of nerve fibrils, before he devised the tissue culture technique (1907). Having solved that problem by relatively simple methods, he found no further incentive to perfect or expand the technique, and turned to other problems amenable to other methods. Carrel, on the other hand, without a specific problem but with a less formulated concept of a vast field of problems, took this technique and perfected it to a very high degree (1912, 1924). The application to new but specific problems again passed to a third set of workers. For example, Fell used it in studying bone phosphatase activity (Fell and Robison, 1929) and local hypervitaminosis (Fell and Mellanby, 1952), Warburg in studying tumor metabolism (Warburg and Kubowitz, 1927; Lipmann, 1932, 1933; Lipmann and Fischer, 1932), Rivers, Haagen, and Muckenfuss (1929), and Li and Rivers (1930) in growing vaccines, Murray and Stout in the diagnosis of tumors (1942, 1947), Gey and Gaillard in studies of endocrine function (Gey, Seeger, and Hellmann, 1938; Stone, Owings, and Gey, 1934a, b; Gaillard, 1948), and Pomerat used it in screening pharmaceutical preparations (1949, 1951). While it is not the function of this book to review these aspects of the field in detail, it may be well to indicate some of the directions which research has already taken and may be expected to take in the future.

Applications of the cell culture technique to date fall for the most part into six categories: (1) cellular nutrition— the degree and manner of dependence of a single cell, type of cell, or tissue on the chemical properties of the external medium; (2) cellular metabolism—those aspects of cellular behavior which have an internal origin and control; (3) hormone relations—the behavior of cells toward the specific products, other than nutrients, of other cells, and the function of cells in producing such products; (4) morphogenesis —the production of integrated patterns of development by the interaction of cells or groups of cells; (5) pathology— the response of cells and tissues to agents of extra-cellular origin which, being neither nutrients, hormones, nor normal self-metabolites, are injurious to the cells in question; and (6) genetics—the behavior of individual cells as bearers of specific inherent characteristics. All of these aspects of cel-- lular activity may be, and many have been, studied in tissue cultures of both plants and animals. And of course none of these can be separated absolutely from the others.

Nutrition

As we have seen elsewhere, that aspect of a culture's reaction to its environment which can be most easily recorded in quantitative terms is its increase in mass. Its alteration in form comes second, while in third rank in ease of investigation but by no means third in importance are its changes in rate of activity as evinced in terms of such factors as enzymatic processes, respiration, photosynthesis (if any), and tropisms.

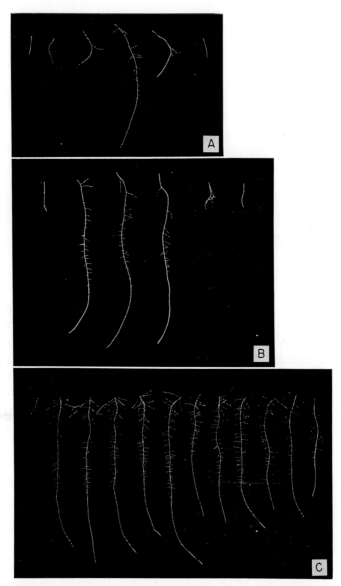

FIGURE 47. Tomato roots grown in nutrients which were alike except for varying concentrations (increasing from left to right) of: A, sucrose; B, iron as $Fe_2(SO_4)_3$; and C, phosphate. The example at the left is in each case the control from which this ingredient has been omitted. The optimal concentration is about 50 mM for sucrose, 0.006 mM for iron, and 0.1 mM for phosphate.

Mass increase has been largely used in measuring the reaction of cultures toward nutrient variables. With plant tissues, in which the entire nutritional pattern has already been largely clarified, mass increase has been used in studying responses to osmotic values, energy levels, nutrient ions, vitamins, nitrogen sources, trace elements, and the like. In this way it has been demonstrated, for example, that whereas the absolute concentrations of the various nutrient ions or molecules which give optimal growth rates of roots differ widely for different substances—50 mM for sucrose (White, 1934a, 1940a, b, 1943b), 20 mM for calcium and magnesium (White, 1933b, 1943b), 0.006 mM for iron (White, 1933b, 1938b, 1943b), 0.00023 mM for thiamine (White, 1937c), and one millionth mM for molybdenum (Boll and Street, 1951)—the range around these optima which will permit "normal" growth is in almost all cases of about the same magnitude, from about 0.5 to 5.0 times the optimal value (1943a, b). The range of capacity of the tissue to adjust its behavior vis-à-vis these widely different substances appears to be about the same, irrespective of the substance under investigation.

These powers of adjustment may be enhanced or reduced according to existing conditions as regards other variables in the environment with which they may have no apparent connection. Thus root cultures grown in a glycine-thiamine nutrient give results which, at their best, are superior to the best results obtained in a complex yeast extract nutrient (White, 1939c), yet in the defined nutrient they appear to be far more sensitive to temperature changes than in the complex nutrient (White, unpublished observations). The presence of large numbers of substances of varied character in the yeast extract seems to "buffer" the cultures against a too great sensitivity to other limiting factors as compared to the relatively few and simple substances in the synthetic (glycine-thiamine) solution. Perhaps this is one reason for past failures to obtain satisfactory growth of animal tissues in simple nutrients. Certain it is that no such clean-cut results have been obtained with animal tissues, although increments have been used in studying responses to salts (Drew, 1923), serum quality and concentration (Ebeling, 1921b), various tissue juices and extracts (Baker and

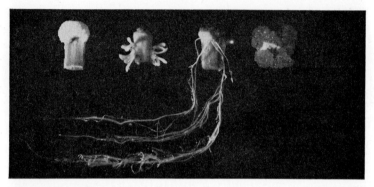

FIGURE 48. Effects of varying the concentrations of adenine and indole acetic acid on the growth *in vitro* of bits of tobacco pith. From left to right: control showing moderately compact callusing; adenine, 40 mg./L. showing production of buds but no roots; indoleacetic acid, 0.08 mg./L. showing production of roots only without buds; and a combination of both adenine and indoleacetic acid in which neither roots nor buds have formed but are replaced by a massive, loose hyperhydric callus. (From Skoog, 1951, Fig. 3A, captions corrected)

Carrel, 1926), break-down products of enzymatic and chemical digestion of proteins (Fischer and Demuth, 1928; Baker and Carrel, 1928), and a few inorganic ions such as magnesium and cobalt (Morgan and Parker, 1952).

Although the general aspects of plant tissue nutrition were fairly well clarified by the studies of White, Robbins, Bonner, and others between 1930 and 1945, there remain many specific problems which are still under investigation. Street and his colleagues (Street and Lowe, 1950; Street and Mc-Gregor, 1952) and Burström (1941a, b) have studied the effects of different sugars on excised roots, have confirmed and enlarged on White's conclusion that sucrose is in most

cases a more suitable source of energy than is dextrose, and
have tied this fact in with the process of phosphorylation

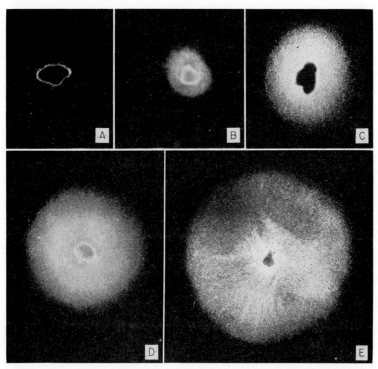

FIGURE 49. Cultures of chick heart fibroblasts cultivated for eight days
in A, A dialyzed serum embryo-extract medium. B, An undialyzed serum
basal medium without embryo extract or other supplementary nutrient materials. C, A dialyzed serum embryo-extract medium (like A) but with pH
corrected by adding Na_2CO_3. D, An undialyzed serum medium (compare
with B) supplemented with "nucleoprotein" material isolated from embryo
extract. E, A complete undialyzed medium containing unfractionated serum
and embryo extract. (A, C, and E from Harris, 1952a, Figs. 2–4; B and D
from Kutsky, 1953, Figs. 2, 3)

(Street, 1950), and the concentrations of inorganic phosphate and iron. Skoog has applied these same correlations
to the morphogenesis of plant callus cultures (Skoog and
Tsui, 1948; Skoog, 1951). Boll has shown that the degree

of dominance of a root apex over lateral roots, and in consequence the relative capacity of such apices to survive as subcultures, is favored by sugar concentrations which fall well below the "optimal" range for short-term mass increase (unpublished, personal communication). Morel has elaborated on the vitamin requirements of callus tissues adding biotin, pantothenic acid, and inositol for some plants such as willow to the three (thiamine, nicotinic acid, and pyridoxin) which are sufficient to satisfy the requirements of most tissues (Morel, 1944b, 1945, 1946; Gautheret, 1950).

The nutrients for animal tissues are less well defined and cannot yet be manipulated with the same precision as can plant tissue nutrients. Nevertheless just this sort of study is one of the major aims of animal cell culture and some progress has been made. Parshley and Simms (1946) report that adult epithelium can be differentially encouraged by increasing the concentration of phosphate in the salt-dextrose diluent. Chèvremont reports that adding choline in large quantity to the nutrient brings about a great increase in the proportion of macrophages in a mixed culture (1943; Frederic, 1951). Fell and Mellanby (1953) report that keratinized skin can be changed to mucoid epithelium by cultivation in massive concentrations of vitamin A.

The growth pattern of chick lymphocytes can be varied so greatly that two cultures are scarcely recognizable as the same kind of cell by varying the source of serum used in the nutrient or by adding substances such as thyroxin to it (Carrel, 1934; Parker, 1950). Skoog has shown that a given plant tissue can be caused to produce roots, leaves, or simple callus by modifying the ratios of phosphate, auxin, sugar, and adenine (1951). A great deal of interest has developed in animal tissue nutrition of late because of the surgical importance of tissue banks, bone banks, skin banks, and the like, which can be made fully successful only by the development of better means of preserving tissues.

Cellular Metabolism

Respiratory mechanisms and enzymatic patterns have in the past been elucidated largely through their study in tissue slices. These of course involve not only an extensive, freshly traumatized surface and a central mass suffering from anoxia but also a mass which is in the process of dying no matter how "normal" its state may momentarily appear to be. A growing tissue culture which has stabilized its relation to its environment should theoretically be a better material for such studies. Tissue cultures have, indeed, been used for this purpose. The study of phosphorylation mechanisms in root cultures has already been mentioned (Street, 1950). Fell and Robison (1929) studied phosphatase activity in cultures of duck bone. Respiratory processes have been studied in plant tissue cultures by Plantefol (1938), Plantefol and Gautheret (1939, 1941), Henderson and Stauffer (1944), and White (1945); these processes have likewise been studied in animal tissues by Lipmann (1932, 1933) and most recently and precisely by Danes and Leinfelder (1951). Water metabolism in plant tissues has been studied in surviving tissue (tissue slices) by Hackett and Thimann (1950), and the special problem of water secretion by roots has been studied by White (1938a). Here again one of the major difficulties in the way of such studies with animal tissues lies in the lack of a precisely defined nutrient substratum in which both growth and normal metabolism can be maintained.

Hormone Relations

This is at present an almost open field. The production of auxins in root cultures was early demonstrated by van Overbeek (1939). Gautheret (1947b, 1948a), de Ropp (1947, 1948), and others have demonstrated in tissue cultures the differences in auxin metabolism between normal and tumor tissues (Kulescha and Gautheret, 1948). Camus has shown the morphogenetic effects of auxin in *in vitro* grafts of plant tissues (Camus, 1949; Camus and Gautheret, 1948a, b). Gey, Seegar, and Hellman (1938), and Jones, Seegar, Gey, and Gey (1942) long ago demonstrated the

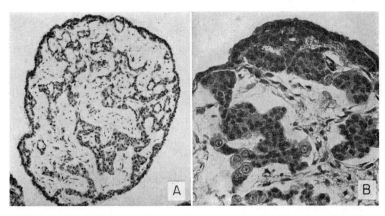

Figure 50. Cultures of human foetal ovaries. A, A section through a six-day-old culture of an ovary of a six-month foetus. The original tissue pattern has disappeared, giving place to a mass of parenchymatous cords separated by connective tissue. B, A higher magnification of a section through a 30-day-old culture showing numerous newly formed oocytes. (Pictures furnished by Prof. P. J. Gaillard)

capacity of glandular tissues to produce hormones *in vitro*, as have Gaillard (1948) and Martinovitch (1938) more recently. The production of insulin by *in vitro* cultures of the Islands of Langerhans of the cat was probably demonstrated by Richardson and Lewis, but in the absence of proper controls was not published. Carrel examined the obverse in studying the effect of insulin on the growth and organization of cultures (Carrel and Lindbergh, 1938), but animal tissue studies of this sort again suffer from the impossibility of controlling absolutely and precisely the hormonal background—the hormonal composition of the classic plasma-embryo-extract substratum. It seems probable that Pomerat's perfusion method (1951), combined with the cellophane technique, may permit short-term studies free of this objection, and that the perfection of satisfactory synthetic nutrients will remove the last major barrier to precise studies of hormonal behavior *in vitro*.

Morphogenesis

It was suggested at the beginning of this volume that the technique of cultivating excised tissues had its chief *raison d'être* and gave its greatest promise in the study of the origins of form and function, that is, in problems of morphogenesis. Harrison's original problem, which led to the first *in vitro* cultivation of animal cells—whether the nerve fibrils originate *in situ* from the innervated cells or their products, or whether they originate *ab extra*, by growth from the distant ganglia—was a morphogenetic problem. So was Robbins' original problem—whether the root was dependent on the leafy portions of the plant for anything more than its basic carbohydrate nutrition. So likewise was the problem—what is the nature of the stimulus by which crown-gall organisms or their products induce abnormal proliferation of the host cells, and ultimately autonomy and malignancy—which led the author of this volume to undertake the development of a plant tissue culture technique. The number of problems which it should be possible to attack by this means is legion.

That the developmental and behavioral pattern in higher animals is greatly influenced by metabolic products known as "hormones" is well known. But how do these effects come about? A defect in the pituitary causes abnormal development of the long bones of the body. Is this a direct effect on the bone cells? That can be tested only in cell cultures. The nearest approach is in the experiments of Fell and Mellanby (1952) in which ossification was reversed and

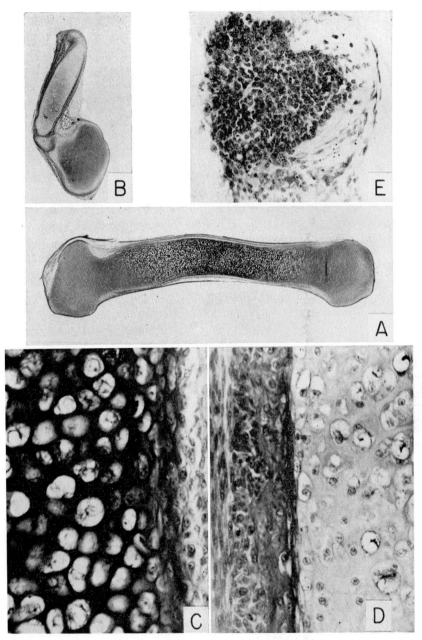

FIGURE 51. (*Explanation on opposite page*)

the cartilage matrix finally left naked when mouse or chick tibias were cultivated in hyper-A-vitaminotic media. Certain of the adrenal hormones and their relatives, such as cortisone, have marked effects in relieving arthritis. Is this a change in degrees or patterns of ossification, or in the texture of inter-ostial tissues, and if the latter, is it neurogenic (antihypertensive), osmotic, or something else? Again, if the effect is a direct one, only cell culture methods will elucidate its nature.

A corresponding picture may be drawn from the point of view of problems of plant morphogenesis. The generalized plant hormone, "auxin," originally studied for its orientation effects (photo- and geotropism) has subsequently come to be looked upon as an important morphogenetic factor. It seems to induce the differentiation of roots from tissues that ordinarily rarely, if ever, produce roots, to control the formation and development of buds, to influence the abscission of leaves and of fruits, to initiate the activity of cambium, to regulate the specific branching habit of plants, to mediate between genes and growing tissues in controlling the erect versus procumbent habit and in producing dwarfness, and to take part in the formation of root nodules. It has been shown to be one of several factors involved in the induction of plant tumors. And it has been shown to control the differentiation of vascular strands induced by in-grafted buds.

←————————————————————————

FIGURE 51. (A-D.) Femurs of six-day chick embryos. A, Control femur grown for nine days in a standard plasma embryo extract medium. B, The opposite femur from the same chick grown in an experimental medium fortified with vitamin A. Note the complete degeneration of the normal shaft. C, A section through the diaphysial region of A. D, The corresponding region of B. E, Terminal cartilage of a foetal mouse radius grown for four days in a hyper-A-vitaminotic medium. A crescent of cartilage at the right was damaged (killed?) in excision and has remained unchanged. In the remainder of the culture, however, the matrix has completely disappeared and the liberated chondroblasts, which appear healthy, are lying free on the surface of the nutrient substratum. A and B, ×19; C and D, ×400; E, ×220. (From Fell and Mellanby, 1952, Figs. 2–4, 22)

The mechanisms of some of these effects can certainly best be studied by use of tissue culture methods. If auxin is truly a specific root-forming hormone, it should be possible to set up conditions under which its local application to an unorganized callus culture would regularly induce the local formation of roots. The cell culture technique seems to offer possibilities for the analysis of these relations under conditions relatively free of uncontrollable variables. The nearest approach to date is the work of Skoog and his group on auxin, phosphate, adenine, and carbohydrate.

This theory of specific inducing substances, however, is countered by a considerable amount of evidence that the formation of organs may also be controlled to some extent, at least, by concentration gradients of non-specific substances, hence by polar (physical) as well as chemical relationships. The cell culture technique thus offers a means of approach to the phenomenon of polarity mentioned at the beginning of this book in connection with the work of Vöchting, Goebel, and others, which was not previously available. Priestley attributed the formation of cambium in radial plant bodies to a radially distributed hydrogen ion gradient (1928). Rosene and Lund have shown that there is a corresponding electrostatic potential gradient which can be modified by imposing artificial oxygen-hydrogen gradients (1931). White has shown that an oxygen gradient may be correlated with the response by which undifferentiated callus cultures are induced to form stems and leaves (1939b). White (1938a) and Rosene (1941; Rosene and Lund, 1935) have shown that there is a hydrostatic flow correlated with the electrostatic gradient along excised and intact roots. But it is as yet quite unknown which of all these gradients—of pH, of redox-potential, of electrostatic potential, of hydrostatic potential, and of tendency to differentiate—is primary and which secondary. It should be possible in cell or tissue cultures artificially to impose or modify any or all of these gradients except the last along controlled spatial axes and thus to determine with which other gradients they bear a causal relationship. Brachet (1937) has applied this method in animal embryology to the study of effects of imposed oxygen gradients. Huxley (1927), Gilchrist (1928), and Vogt (1932) have applied it to the study of temperature gradients. Weiss has studied the orientation of animal cell cultures in response to lines of tension in the medium (Weiss, 1929). Fife and Frampton (1936) applied it in plant pathology to the study of the causal factors involved in the orientation of a parasitic insect's proboscis in the tissues of the host, with brilliant results.

This matter of organization has been applied in an interesting way by Pomerat. Taking a culture of cat brain and growing it in a dilute plasma clot on a cover slip in a roller tube it is possible to establish a culture which, when it reaches a diameter of 3–4 mm., becomes "stabilized." It takes on a definite pattern with large "protective" cells oriented in radial fashion but with a crenellated margin at the outside. Next to these is a ring of smaller glial cells generally oriented tangentially, forming a fairly wide compact ring of small cells. The center is traversed by radial or randomly anastomosing long strands of nerves and interspersed with these there is a constantly moving, circulating mass of fibroblasts, lymphocytes, and glia. Motion pictures show that all of these, with the exception of the nerves, are in a constant state of flux, that there is a constant traffic across this central area, an exchange between center and margins, and around the margin. Yet the general pattern is stable for weeks on end. The pattern appears to be a matter of organization and the culture is itself a complex, well-integrated organism. Plant callus cultures, though lacking the possibility of internal movement, sometimes show a surprisingly similar over-all pattern of organization.

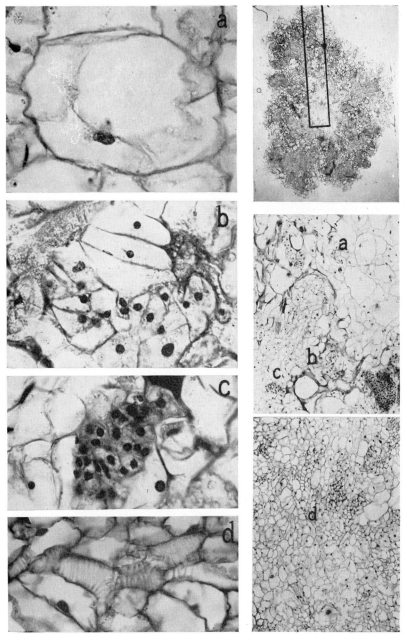

FIGURE 52A. (*Explanation on opposite page*)

One method of approach to problems of organization which has proved especially effective in animal embryology is, as we have seen, that of transplantation, developed to a high degree by Harrison and Spemann. The technique developed consecutively by Boysen-Jensen, Paal, and Went, of transplanting *Avena* coleoptile tips or agar blocks containing extracts from such tips is essentially a comparable technique, the coleoptile or agar block acting in the same way as an organizer in the sense of Spemann. The method of cultivating tissues of endocrines in the serum of an anticipated recipient and then implanting in such a recipient, developed by Stone, Owings, and Gey (1934a, b), and by Gaillard (1948), is an extension of this approach, as is Camus' implantation of excised buds into plant tissue cultures (1949).

Another related field is the transplantation or explantation of eggs and young embryos. In animals this has involved the transplantation of an ovum (fertilized or unfertilized) from one female to another (mouse, rabbit, etc.). This has been done either to overcome physiological problems in the donor, such as a tendency to early abortion, or to study the relative importance of certain hereditary versus maternal environmental factors in subsequent development. This second objective has not been studied in plants, but a great deal of important work has been done on the first, involving cell

FIGURE 52A. Structural organization in culture. A culture isolated from the procambial region of an individual of the hybrid tobacco *Nicotiana glauca* × *N. Langsdorffii*. At the upper right is a horizontal section through an eight-week-old culture, ×10. The two pictures below are from the area blocked out in this picture and are reproduced ×70. The four figures at the left are representative of the regions lettered and are ×435. At the margin are many large cells (*a*) which arise by hyperhydric enlargement of parenchyma cells and are apparently moribund. At (*b*) large cells have divided and at (*c*) division has become still more active, forming nests of dense, meristematic cells. In the center of the culture, on the other hand, the cells are stabilized and in some cases (*d*) have differentiated into incipient conducting strands of scalariform cells. Such a pattern is repeated in each culture and shows the tendency to organize into societies of cells with some segregation of function. (Saffanin-Delafield's haematoxylin) culture methods. Thus Tukey with stone-fruits (1933, 1934), van Overbeek, Conklin, and Blakeslee (1941, 1942) with *Datura,* Nickell with apple (1951), Brink, Cooper, and Ausherman (1944) with grains, and others, have removed the embryos from normally aborting hybrid strains of plants and by cultivating these embryos *in vitro* have been able to bring them to maturity and thus to produce progeny from ordinarily "infertile" hybrids, comparable in result to the maintenance of the "temperamentally infertile," "obese" mouse at the Jackson Laboratory.

Pathology

A great many problems in both gross and cellular pathology, but especially the latter, can best be approached at the cellular level. There exist in animals two types of immunity: (1) "humoral" immunity dependent on circulating antibodies in the blood, and (2) cellular immunity, which resides in the affected cells themselves. Only the latter type is represented

---→

FIGURE 52B. Structural organization in culture. A culture isolated from the cerebellar folia of a newborn kitten. At the upper left is a picture of a 41-day-old culture grown on a cover-glass strip inserted in a roller tube. ×5. The figure below represents the area blocked out in this picture and is reproduced ×40. The four figures at the right are representative of the regions lettered and are ×200. At the margin (*a*) there are large epithelioid cells which anchor the colony to the plasma clot. These are believed to be pial in origin. The darkly stained cell is probably a neuron of the stellate type. The submarginal zone (*b*) contains many closely packed astrocytes and occasional neural strands. The dark-stained cell at the center is a granule cell. Below this (*c*) is a region in which the clot is markedly liquefied, and is characterized by a loose glial organization with argentophilic cells believed to be Golgi Type II neurons. The center of the culture (*d*) is made up of criss-crossed fibers, Purkinje cells, and glial cells.

The over-all pattern is relatively stabile, the epithelioid marginal cells and the neural fibers showing little change from day to day, yet cinematographs show that the glial cells are constantly moving about like pedestrians in a busy city. The regular development of this pattern suggests the possibility of analyzing complex patterns *in vitro* in terms of "societal cytology."

(Bodian technique. Published by permission of C. M. Pomerat from unpublished data.)

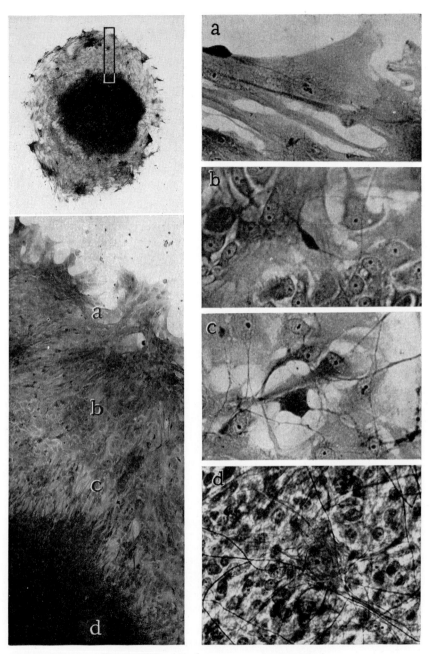

FIGURE 52B. (*Explanation on opposite page*)

in plants (Chester, 1933; Price, 1940). Even the antibodies themselves are probably produced in or at least on the surface of living cells. This question of antibody formation has been studied somewhat in cell culture but mostly without as satisfactory results as were hoped for, largely probably

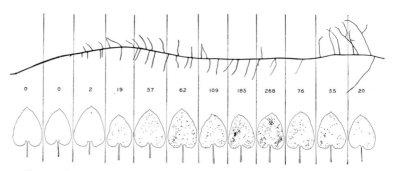

FIGURE 53. Titration of aucuba mosaic virus propagated in excised tomato roots grown *in vitro*. A root was isolated from a systemically infected plant so that it carried the virus permanently in all parts. After being cultivated for 25 passages, a typical root about 120 mm. long was divided into 10-mm. segments and each segment was crushed and rubbed into a leaf of *Nicotiana glutinosa*. The number of local lesions produced at the end of 36 hours (numbers) gives a measure of the number of free virus particles per segment. The virus concentration is very low in the rapidly growing apex, high in the maturing regions 8–10 cm. back of the tip, and apparently low in the oldest basal region. Since, however, this last is the region in which massive "striate bodies" make their appearance, this apparent drop is probably no more than a result of aggregation of many units into single masses. (From White, 1943a, Fig. 59)

because of the complexities and imprecisions of current techniques. One of the best examples is Harris' demonstration that the incompatibilities which prevent heteroplastic grafts between rat and mouse, for example, are not cellular in origin since tissues of the two genera grown together in culture intermix freely and apparently permanently without any evident reaction (1943).

Of far greater present importance is the use of either true cell cultures or a modified tissue-survival method in the propagation of viruses and the production of vaccines. Li and Rivers (1930) produced a vaccine to vaccinia virus *in vitro* in 1930. White used excised root cultures as a means of propagating tobacco mosaic virus *in vitro;* of titrating its progressive migration in growing tissues (1934b); and, with Stanley, of demonstrating the fact that the process of virus multiplication is independent of host species and of photosynthetic mechanisms (Stanley, 1938). A corresponding technique has recently become very important indeed in the propagation, study, and preparation of vaccines against such viruses as poliomyelitis (Weller, 1953; Weller and Enders, 1948), herpes (Robbins and Enders, 1950), and mumps (Gey and Bang, 1951). Attempts have been made repeatedly to cultivate the virus of the common cold in cell cultures but without complete satisfaction. Morel has used tissue cultures of grape as a substratum on which to cultivate the fungus causing mildew, *Peronospora viticola* (1944a, 1948).

Many processes of parasitism should be studied in this way. From quite a different point of view, the direct effects of a large spectrum of damaging agents, both inorganic and organic, on cells are under investigation. The Sloan-Kettering Institute's program of screening carcinogens, steroids, carcinostatic agents, and the like, by use of cell culture methods is an example (Biesele, 1951). One of the most promising approaches is that developed by Pomerat (1951) for the study of antihistaminics and similar pharmacologically active agents (Painter, Pomerat, and Ezell, 1949).

One field in which tissue culture has given particular promise is that of the study of the processes of carcinogenesis. This has been attacked directly by Earle, applying known carcinogens to healthy cells *in vitro* (1943). Carcinogenesis was demonstrated in this way, but since it also appears to have occurred spontaneously and repeatedly in tissue cultures in the laboratories of Earle (1943b) and of Gey (Firor and Gey, 1945), the significance of this result is still uncertain. A somewhat similar result has occurred with plant tissues in the laboratories of Gautheret, where tissues of carrot (Gautheret), grape (Morel), *Scorzonera* (Camus and Gautheret, 1948c), tobacco (Limasset and Gautheret, 1950), and other plants have undergone a spontaneous and permanent change, acquiring the capacity to synthesize excess quantities of auxin, which is one of the

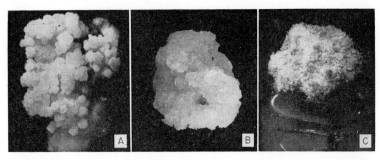

FIGURE 54. Cultures of grape, *Vitis vinifera*. A, Normal tissue, requiring auxin in the nutrient in order to continue growth. B, "Habituated" tissue derived from (A) but which has spontaneously altered its metabolism so that it now requires no external source of auxin and in fact now manufactures a measurable excess of auxin. C, A culture of normal tissue inoculated with grape mildew, *Peronospora viticola*, an obligate parasite. This thus provides the first successful continuous laboratory culture of the fungus. (From Morel, 1948, Plate XIII, A, B; XX A)

distinguishing features of tumorous as opposed to normal tissues. The tissue culture method has been used by White and Braun (1942) for the propagation of plant tumor tissues and the demonstration of their malignancy. Similarly, cell culture is a major tool in the propagation of animal tumors, and in the hands of Murray and Stout (1942, 1947), and others, has served as an important tool in the diagnosis of certain obscure neuromas and other tumors. It has also been used by Porter, Claude, and Fullam (1945), Porter and Thompson (1947), Bang and Gey (1949), and others, in the electron-microscope study of the inclusions which may accompany certain tumors such as the Rous sarcoma of fowls.

Genetics

Both in plants and animals the problems of sterility are major ones. Particularly in hybridization studies a considerable proportion of theoretical progenies fail to develop, owing to abortion. In plants this is often the result of failure of the nutritive tissues to develop properly. In animals it may be due to inadequate implantation and vascularization, or to hormonal imbalances in the mother. In either case potentially valuable progeny may be lost. And in both cases the embryos themselves are often perfectly viable, the fault lying in the maternal organism itself. Theoretically it should be possible, by the use of refined cell culture techniques, to remove the egg cell after fertilization and cultivate it *in vitro*, bringing it to maturity and adulthood. To date this has not been possible with either plants or animals. The same end is accomplished with animals by the transplantation of unfertilized eggs from the body of an aborting or otherwise "infertile" mother to a "fertile" foster mother in whose body the egg can then be fertilized and raised. This has been done with mice (Runner, unpublished), rabbits (Chang, 1948, 1950; Chang and Pincus, 1951), cattle (Chang and Pincus, 1951), and others. One of the dramatic results of this technique is the raising of experimental supplies of obese mice which are genetically fertile but mechanically unable to mate.

With plants somewhat better "cell culture" results have been obtained. While it is not yet possible to remove an egg cell, either before or after fertilization, or even a proembryo or a very young embryo and grow it successfully, it is possible to begin with the early torpedo stage, just after the formation of the cotyledons. Embryos of cherry, peach, plum (Tukey), apple (Nickell), *Datura* (Blakeslee), *Iris* (Randolph), various grasses (Brink and others), and other plants have thus been excised and grown. This has permitted the study of "physiologically sterile" hybrids of *Datura* and *Prunus,* and has greatly accelerated breeding programs with prairie grasses whose prolonged dormancy (often several years when left in the seed coat) has been a serious barrier.

These are given merely as examples of the many fields of investigation in which the techniques of cell culture have already found wide usefulness and in which improvements in methods, particularly increased mastery of the nutritional problems involved, may be expected to extend that usefulness. The field should certainly develop rapidly in the coming years.

Appendix.

SOME SIMPLE TECHNIQUES
FOR BEGINNERS

THE INTENTION of this book, as set forth in the Foreword, has been to make available the techniques of cell culture, and to show that these methods are neither difficult nor sacrosanct. It therefore seems not amiss to append a few short "exercises for class use." I have tried to choose examples which are as simple as possible, so that they will not be beyond the physical means of small schools. At the same time, I have tried to formulate exercises which are typical of large groups of problems, and of all the general types which the student is likely to encounter. They should be sufficient to serve as foundation stones upon which wider, more varied and imaginative, and more specialized studies can be based.

Plant Cultures

A single stock nutrient will suffice for all plant cell cultures with which the beginner needs to acquaint himself, requiring only minor changes for particular uses.

Prepare the following stock solutions:

A. A standard salt solution (page 74)
B. An organic accessory solution (page 74)
C. Stock solutions of calcium pantothenate, biotin, and naphthalene acetic acid (page 75)

Have ready twenty-four 125-ml. Erlenmeyer flasks, fifty-two lipless 25 by 150-mm. test tubes, six 100-mm. Petri dishes, sixteen U. S. Bureau of Plant Industry watch glasses (Fig. 30A), and two battery jars, all sterile.

Dissolve 10 mg. of ferric sulfate [$Fe_2(SO_4)_3$] in 200 ml. of water; discard 100 ml. Dissolve 40 g. of sucrose in 500 ml. of water. Dissolve 4 g. of Difco "Noble" agar in 400 ml. of water. To the 500 ml. of sugar solution add the 100 ml. of ferric sulfate solution, 200 ml. of salt solution A, 2 ml. of accessory solution B, and make up with water to one liter. Divide this into two parts of 600 and 400 ml. each. Dilute the larger portion 1:1 to make 1200 ml. Distribute 1000 ml. in 50-ml. portions to 20 of the 125-ml. flasks, plug with cotton covered with gauze, cap with 50-ml. beakers (small "Dixie" cups will serve the same purpose) to keep out dust, and autoclave at 18 pounds pressure for 20 minutes. The remaining 200 ml. of nutrient should be distributed in 10-ml. portions to 20 test tubes, plugged, and autoclaved. To the 400-ml. portion of nutrient add the 400 ml. of agar, hot. Distribute 600 ml. of this agar nutrient in 15-ml. portions to 40 test tubes. To the remaining 200 ml. add 2 ml. each of calcium pantothenate, biotin, and naphthalene acetic acid solutions, mix thoroughly, and distribute in 15-ml. samples to 13 test tubes. Plug and autoclave as before. (These should solidify satisfactorily. If they do not, it is probable that the nutrient as made up is too acid. The acidity may be as low as 5.5. If it is any lower than this, it should be adjusted with 0.1 N NaOH.)

We now have:

24 125-ml. flasks of liquid nutrient of standard formula.

12 large test tubes of liquid nutrient, also of standard formula.

40 test tubes of agar nutrient of the same nutritional formula.

13 test tubes of agar nutrient containing pantothenate, biotin, and NAA in addition to the standard ingredients.

These will suffice for cultures of all the plant tissues and organs with which we will wish to deal in this section.

Tomato Roots.—METHOD A. Take a sound, ripe tomato, wash carefully, wipe dry. Cut the skin fairly deep, beginning about ½ inch from the stem and running upward to the flower end, on four different sectors dividing the tomato into quarters. Break the fruit open, laying the sectors back and being careful that the exposed seeds are not touched by instruments, fingers, or by the outer, possibly non-sterile surfaces of the fruit. With sterile forceps remove 25 seeds and place in five Petri dishes lined with sterile Whatman No. 1 or other coarse filter paper moistened with sterile water. Set aside in the dark at room temperature. The seeds should germinate within a few days. When the roots are 2–3 cm. long, select ten of the best, sever them with a sharp scalpel, and transfer individually to as many flasks of nutrient. Some of these should grow and at the end of a week one-cm. tips either of the main root or of well-established branches can be selected, severed with a pair of scissors, and transferred to fresh nutrient. Such clones of roots should grow indefinitely if properly handled. They can be used for many kinds of nutritional and morphogenetic studies.

METHOD B. Make six straight cuttings from a healthy tomato plant and remove the leaves. Wash thoroughly with 1:10 solution of "Clorox," rinse with sterile water, and shake off the surplus. Insert these cuttings firmly, stem end up, in holes in two sheets of heavy, paraffined cardboard a little larger than the battery jars so that about 25 cm. of stem protrudes downward. Line the jars with sterile blotting paper, add about 3 cm. of sterile water in the bottom, and cover with the cardboards so that the tomato stems hang in the moist interior. Set aside in the dark at room temperature. Roots should appear in about 10 days. When they are 3–5 cm. long, select ten sound-appearing roots, cut them carefully with sterile scissors at a length of about 1 cm., and drop the severed tips into as many flasks of nutrient. Some of them may be contaminated with epiphytic molds or bacteria, but some will be sterile and should grow well. These can also be used as starting material for clones capable of un-limited survival and growth.

Chickweed Embryos.—Prepare two Petri dishes, each pro-vided with eight miniature Syracuse watch glasses. Melt a tube of standard nutrient agar, without accessory vitamins, and place one ml. in each watch glass.

The common chickweed, *Stellaria media,* can usually be found blooming at any season of the year except midwinter, in any community, in lawns, at the edges of gardens, around shrubs, and similar places. Bring in a healthy plant and with tweezers pick off a dozen sound seed pods, choosing those which are young enough to have the remains of the corolla still present and not completely shriveled. Wash briefly in 1:10 "Clorox" and transfer to sterile water. Keep covered. Place a sterile glass plate on the stage of the dissecting microscope and add a large drop of sterile water. Transfer a seed pod to this drop; then, holding it lightly with mosquito forceps in the left hand, with a cataract knife or other small knife (excellent ones can be made by grinding flat blades on the ends of large sewing needles) cut off the end of the pod. Then with a fine needle pull out the seeds. These should be transferred to a hollow-ground slide or small watch class containing sterile nutrient (use a few drops of nutrient from one of the Erlenmeyers). When a sufficient number has been isolated, prepare a fresh plate with a drop of nutrient (just enough to keep the seeds moist). Transfer a seed to this drop—the seeds will be about one mm. in diam-eter—and again with fine forceps and small knife remove a narrow sector adjacent to the micropyle and toward the chalazal end. Then pressing with the flat of the knife over the micropyle, the embryo will be forced around and out through the cut surface. As each embryo is removed, it is transferred to a watch glass of agar in one of the Petri dishes and covered with a one-inch round No. 2 cover glass. Use a fresh drop of sterile nutrient for the dissection of each seed and be sure that all instruments are dipped in boiling water after each dissection. Two sets of instruments will facilitate this. When 16 embryos have been dissected, put a little sterile water in each Petri dish around the watch glasses to maintain a high humidity, cover, and set aside in the dark at room temperature. These embryos, if uninjured and aseptic, should grow. They can be transferred to larger watch glasses, to flasks, or they can be cut up and used to start further cultures.

Embryos of purslane (*Portulaca oleracea*), another common weed, can also be used. The embryos of the larger grasses and sedges and of many garden plants are also satisfactory material for the beginner.

Carrot Callus.—Fold ten 60 by 60-mm. squares of filter paper lengthwise twice to expose a final surface of 15 by 60 mm., sterilize, and insert in as many 25 by 150-mm. tubes of liquid nutrient. Select a sound crisp carrot about 6 inches long, wash thoroughly, dry, and break in the middle. This exposes an aseptic broken surface. With a sterile cork-borer 3–5 mm. in diameter remove a series of cores, so placed that the cambium traverses them lengthwise. As these are removed, transfer them to a sterile Petri dish. Then with a sharp scalpel make a series of transverse cuts in these cores, one mm. apart, forming disks of tissue. Transfer two of these disks to each fold of paper and set the tubes aside, sloped at about 15° from the horizontal so that the paper dips into and is kept moist by the nutrient but the disks of tissue are not immersed therein. These should form extensive callus within about two weeks. This callus can then be removed for subculturing. It will not grow indefinitely on this simple nutrient (unless it has undergone the as yet unexplained change called "habituation" by Gautheret); but if transferred to a nutrient supplemented with naphthalene acetic acid, it will establish clones capable of unlimited survival and growth.

Willow Cambium.—Select in the field a sound young willow (*Salix nigra* is excellent; in Europe *Salix capraea* has been much used). Cut and bring into the laboratory a piece of branch a foot or more long and from 1 to 3 inches in diameter. Wash thoroughly and dry. Then make two encircling incisions about an inch and a half apart and a single intersecting longitudinal incision. Peel the bark (this of course is easiest in the spring, as makers of willow whistles know), being careful that the exposed cambium touches no contaminated surface or instrument. Pin the bark out flat on a soft pine or cork board. With a sharp sterile scalpel make a series of cross-hatching shallow incisions about 2–3 mm. apart. Six such incisions each way will cut out 25 squares of phloem tissue. Lift these out to a depth of about half the thickness of the bark. With tweezers transfer these to tubes of agar supplemented with biotin, Ca-pantothenate, and NAA, setting the blocks on edge and pushing them into the agar so that they are about half exposed and half buried. Set aside in the dark at room temperature. Proliferation should occur at and just above the agar level, the new growth spreading out over the agar. At the end of about a month this new growth can be excised and transferred to fresh nutrient.

Sunflower Secondary Tumors.—(This exercise is added for those who care to attempt a manipulation which requires somewhat more time but is of considerable interest.)

Plant six seeds of "giant Russian sunflower" (*Helianthus annuus*) in each of ten 6-inch pots of good soil. When sprouted and well established, thin to one good plant per pot. When the stems are 4 inches high above the cotyledons, inoculate each plant just above the cotyledons with a single needle puncture of a 48-hour broth culture of *Agrobacterium tumefaciens,* the crown-gall bacterium. Tumors will develop at the point of inoculation. After about six weeks some plants, varying from 10 to 60 per cent, should develop bacteria-free secondary tumors at the bases of the petioles of one or more leaves above the site of inoculation. Choose one or more plants so affected, cut off 6 inches above and below the secondary tumor, and bring into the laboratory. Split the stem an inch or more beginning at the basal end in a plane passing through the tumor, then by careful tearing cause the split to continue through or behind the tumor, exposing the tumor's interior. Then with a sharp-pointed knife remove bits of tissue a millimeter or more on a side from this exposed interior and transfer to tubes of unsupplemented agar nutrient. Some of these are likely to be contaminated with casual epiphytic fungi and bacteria, but a considerable proportion should be sterile and some will grow into massive cultures of disorganized tissue. These grow rapidly in standard unsupplemented nutrient and are highly malignant, as shown by their formation of massive sterile tumors upon implantation under the bark of healthy sunflower plants.

Animal Cultures

Prepare and have available:

Chick plasma (fresh, or lyophilized and reconstituted).
Chick or horse serum.
Chick embryo extract (fresh, or lyophilized and reconstituted).
A nutrient salt solution (Earle's, White's, or Tyrode's, page 90).
A synthetic nutrient solution of the White type (pages 94–95).

Depression slides, cover slips, 16 by 150-mm. Pyrex test tubes, miniature Syracuse watch glasses, Carrel flasks, and the necessary implements, stoppers, pipettes, etc.

Chick Heart.—Open six embryonated hen's eggs which have been incubated for 6 days, remove the hearts to a watch glass containing salt solution (Earle's, for example), transfer them through two changes of solution to remove excess blood, then transfer to a dry watch glass (Columbia type) or a depression slide, and cut up with sharp scissors or with two scalpels.

Hanging-Drop Cultures.—Lay out six 22 by 22-mm. cover glasses and two Petri dish covers (sterile). With a pipette, or better still a one-ml. tuberculin syringe with a No. 26 needle, apply a drop of embryo extract to the center of each cover slip. Apply a ring of six such drops equally spaced on the interior surface of each of two Petri dish covers. Place a bit of heart tissue in each drop, then add a drop of plasma to each, stir quickly, and allow them to clot. A drop of nutrient salt solution should then be added to each. Invert a depression slide, with a drop of vaseline on each side of the depression, over each cover slip, then invert the slides, bringing the cover slips upward and seal with hot paraffin-vaseline mixture (3:1). Invert the bottoms of the Petri dishes into the tops and seal with twine dipped in hot paraffin. Set slides and Petri dishes in an incubator at 37°C. They should be observed daily. They will serve for class observation and study for several days without any attention. If they are to be kept for longer study, the nutrient must be renewed twice weekly and the cultures cut up and transferred whenever they attain diameters of 5 mm. or more.

Roller Tube Cultures.—Place four bits of heart tissue in a row along one side of the interior of each of twenty 16 by 150-mm. Pyrex test tubes. To ten tubes add a drop of embryo extract and a drop of plasma to each bit of tissue. The other ten will be left without clot. Stopper both sets and allow them to stand for one hour. Then add one ml. of nutrient to each. For five cultures with clot and five without, the nutrient should consist of 60 per cent salt solution (Earle's, Tyrode's, etc.) : 20 per cent serum : 20 per cent embryo extract. The other ten (five of each group) should be charged with an equal quantity of synthetic nutrient. Place the tubes in a roller-tube rotor at 37°C. If a rotor is not available they may be set at a slight slope, tissue down, in any incubator, but in that case only those bits of tissue toward the mouth of the tube under a shallow layer of nutrient can be expected to grow. These cultures should likewise be examined daily and the nutrient renewed, if so desired, once or twice a week.

Chick Lung.—Lung tissue is better taken from somewhat older embryos than heart tissue. Open six embryonated eggs which have been incubated for 12 days, remove the embryos, and dissect out the lungs, wash through several changes of salt solution or synthetic nutrient, and cut up quite fine. From this point the procedure is exactly the same as for the heart tissue. Lung tissue is particularly valuable to demonstrate peristalsis, which will usually be active during the first two or three days, and ciliary activity, which generally does not become evident until about the eighth day.

Chick Striated Muscle.—Muscle should be taken from 10-day embryos and is particularly satisfactory for Carrel flask cultures. Open four 10-day eggs, remove the embryos, dissect off the skin of the legs, cut them at "heel" and "hip," and transfer to a watch glass. Here the bones are removed and discarded. The muscle is then washed and cut up. Cultures can be prepared as hanging drops, in roller tubes, or in Carrel flasks. To each of six Carrel flasks with perforated cellophane inserts add 1 ml. of nutrient. Take up the tissue in a straight pipette and inoculate under the cellophane, pushing the cellophane down afterward to spread the tissue. These cultures should show muscular twitching for several days, and in the classic nutrient (serum : embryo extract : salt solution) will establish permanent strains of fibroblasts.

Mouse Skin.—A mouse, 16 to 18 days pregnant, is killed and opened, the uterus removed intact to a Petri dish, and the embryos removed and placed in a small dish with enough salt solution to keep them moist. Strips of skin are then dissected off and cut into squares 1–2 mm. on a side. Twelve narrow cover slips, 5 by 40 mm., are laid across a large slide, a drop of water under each serving to hold them by capillarity. Six drops of embryo extract are placed in a row on each cover slip, a bit of skin spread out in each drop, and a drop of plasma added to each. They are allowed to clot. The cover slips are then taken up in pairs, are placed back to back, and slid into 16 by 150-mm. test tubes (each with 1 or 2 ml. of nutrient) and the tubes placed in a rotor or incubator at 37°C. These cultures cannot be studied satisfactorily in the tubes, but they can be removed at intervals and either fixed and stained or mounted as elongated temporary hanging-drop cultures, and observed under the high power of the microscope. They should show migration of epithelial sheets as well as fibroblasts and some subcutaneous muscle.

Chick Bone.—The same embryos can be used for these cultures as for those of heart tissue, since six-day bones are quite suitable. The legs should be severed at the hip and set aside in a watch glass. The flesh and skin are then carefully dissected away from the bones, under the binocular, and the bones are separated at the joints and carefully washed. A series of small watch glasses in Petri dishes are provided with firm clots consisting of 60 per cent nutrient salt solution, 20 per cent plasma, and 20 per cent embryo extract well mixed and allowed to coagulate. The bones are laid on the surface of this clot, and the dishes covered with one-inch round cover glasses. Experience has shown that the bones should be moved, if only slightly, each day, so as to establish fresh surfaces of contact with the substratum and to minimize the formation of a halo of fibroblast growth which, if allowed to become established, will not only exhaust the substratum but will tend to distort the developmental pattern of the bone. Such cultures can be maintained, their development observed, and if desired their metabolism followed for several weeks. A similar technique can be used for cultivating organs such as ovaries, eyes, and teeth.

Virus Cultures

Like the cultures from crown-gall tumors of plants, this exercise is introduced for the benefit of those whose special interests may induce them to attempt a rather specialized problem which is, in this case, not a true cell or tissue culture but rather the use of surviving cells for the propagation of a particular agent. For this purpose any of the common viruses—vaccinia, mumps, encephalitis, foot-and-mouth disease, polio—may be used, with slight modifications. As a class exercise vaccinia may be one of the most easily available and least dangerous. Two methods should be tried.

1. Flask Method (Maitland).—Charge five 125-ml. Erlenmeyer flasks, each with 10 ml. of a balanced salt solution (Earle's solution) or a more complex synthetic nutrient (White's nutrient). To this add a 1-ml. suspension of chopped rabbit kidney, prepared aseptically, and 1 ml. of an active culture of vaccinia virus (such as is represented by a suspension of dried [lyophilized] skin from an active lesion), mix thoroughly, and set aside at 37°C. At the end of a week 1 ml. of fluid drawn from such a flask can be used as inoculum for a second series. Titration in susceptible animals will show that the virus has multiplied during the interval, although the number of viable host cells will have decreased to a considerable degree—even to the point of complete disappearance. Large test tubes can also be used for such cultures but provide less satisfactory conditions for cell survival.

2. Roller Tube Method.—Prepare a series of cultures of embryo rabbit skin on plasma clots either in standard roller tubes or on strip cover glasses (see page 140). Charge the tubes with a nutrient consisting of 60 per cent salt solution : 20 per cent serum : 20 per cent embryo extract. When growth is well established (8–10 days, 2–3 renewals of nutrient), add 0.1 ml. of a suspension of lyophilized vaccinia-infected tissue to each tube. The virus will quickly establish itself in the growing epithelium and can be propagated for long periods. Similar cultures, using human skin, have been used for propagating polio virus. The tubes need not be rotated; but if they are not, only those cultures growing near the mouth of the tube (that is, those under a relatively shallow layer of nutrient) will survive and grow.

BIBLIOGRAPHY

ALMQUIST, H. J., and C. R. GRAU. 1944. The amino acid requirements of the chick. *J. Nutrition* **28:** 325–331.

ARCHIBALD, R. M. 1945. Chemical characteristics and physiological rôles of glutamine. *Chem. Rev.* **37:** 161–208.

ARISTOTLE. 360 B.C. *Historia animalium.* Tr. by d'Arcy W. Thompson. Oxford: The Clarendon Press, 1910.

ARNOLD, J. 1887. Ueber Theilungsvorgänge an den Wanderzellen, ihre progressiven und retrogressiven Metamorphosen. *Arch. mikr. Anat.* **30:** 205–326.

BAKER, J. R. 1952. The cell theory. A restatement, history and critique. III, The cell as a morphological unit. *J. Microscop. Sci.* **93:** 157–190.

BAKER, L. E. 1936. Artificial media for the cultivation of fibroblasts, epithelial cells and monocytes. *Sci.* **83:** 605–606.

BAKER, L. E., and A. CARREL. 1926. Effect of the amino acids and hydrolyzable constituents of embryonic tissue juice on the growth of fibroblasts. *J. Exp. Med.* **44:** 397–407.

———. 1928. Effect of liver and pituitary digests on the proliferation of sarcomatous fibroblasts of the rat. *J. Exp. Med.* **47:** 371–378.

BAKER, L. E., and A. H. Ebeling. 1939. Artificial maintenance media for cell and organ cultivation. I, The cultivation of fibroblasts in artificial and serumless media. *J. Exp. Med.* **69:** 365–378.

BANG, F. B., and G. O. GEY. 1949. Electron microscopy of tissue cultures infected with the virus of eastern equine encephalomyelitis. *Proc. Soc. Exp. Biol. Med.* **71:** 78–80.

BARSKI, G., and P. MANIGAULT. 1951. Méthode photométrique d'évaluation de croissance tissulaire *in vitro* en culture sur membranes plastiques. *Ann. Inst. Pasteur* **81:** 1–10.

BARSKI, G., and J. MAURIN. 1948. Culture sur membranes plastiques en milieu liquide de différents tissus: tissu nerveux et mesenchymateux. *Ann. Inst. Pasteur* **74:** 312–322.

BARSKI, G., J. MAURIN, G. WIELGOSZ, and P. LÉPINE. 1951. Conditions de nutrition cellulaire *in vitro* en culture sans support plasmatique. Rôle des fractions micro- et macro-moléculaires. *Ann. Inst. Pasteur* **81:** 9–24.

BERNARD, CLAUDE. 1872. *De la physiologie générale.* Paris: Hachette.

———. 1878–79. *Leçons sur les phénomènes de la vie communs aux animaux et aux végétaux.* Paris: Baillière. (2 vols.)

BERTHELOT, A. 1934. Nouvelles remarques d'ordre chimique sur le choix des milieux de culture naturels et sur la manière de formuler les milieux synthétiques. *Bull. Soc. Chim. biol.*, Paris, **16:** 1553–1557.

BIESELE, J. J. 1951. Tissue culture screening of agents in experimental cancer chemotherapy. *Methods Med. Res.* **4:** 272–275.

BOLL, W. G., and H. E. Street. 1951. Studies on the growth of excised roots. I, The stimulatory effect of molybdenum and copper on the growth of excised tomato roots. *New Phytol.* **50**: 52–75.

BONNER, J., and F. ADDICOTT. 1937. Cultivation *in vitro* of excised pea roots. *Bot. Gaz.* **99**: 144–170.

BORODIN, J. 1878. Ueber die physiologische Rolle und die Verbreitung des Asparagins im Pflanzenreiche. *Bot. Zeitng.* **36**: 801–832.

BRACHET, J. 1937. Some oxidative properties of isolated amphibian germinal vesicles. *Sci.* **86**: 225.

BRINK, R. A., D. C. COOPER, and L. E. AUSHERMAN. 1944. A hybrid between *Hordeum jubatum* and *Secale cereale* reared from an artificially cultivated embryo. *J. Hered.* **35**: 67–75.

BROWN, ROBERT. 1833. Observations on the organs and mode of fecundation in Orchideae and Asclepiadeae. *Trans. Linnean Soc.* **16**: 685–745.

BRYANT, J. C., W. R. EARLE, and E. V. PEPPERS. 1953. The effect of ultracentrifugation and hyaluronidase on the filtrability of chick embryo extract for tissue culture. *J. Nat. Cancer. Inst.* **14**: 189–225.

BUCHSBAUM, R., and C. LOOSLI. 1936. *Methods of tissue culture* in vitro. Chicago: Univ. of Chicago Press.

BURROWS, M. T. 1910a. The cultivation of tissues of the chick embryo outside the body. *J. Am. Med. Assoc.* **55**: 2057–2058.

———. 1910b. Culture des tissus d'embryon de poulet et spécialement cultures de nerfs de poulet en dehors de l'organisme. *C.r. Soc. Biol.*, Paris, **69**: 291–292.

———. 1911. The growth of tissues of the chick embryo outside the animal body, with special reference to the nervous system. *J. Exp. Zool.* **10**: 63–84.

BURSTRÖM, H. 1941a. Formative effects of carbohydrates on root growth. *Bot. Notiser.* 1941(3): 310–334.

———. 1941b. Studies on the carbohydrate nutrition of roots. *Ann. Agric. College of Sweden* **9**: 264–284.

CAMERON, GLADYS. 1950. *Tissue culture technique.* New York: Academic Press, Inc.

CAMUS, G. 1949. Recherches sur le rôle des bourgeons dans les phénomènes de morphogénèse. *Rev. Cytol. et Biol. veget.* **11**: 1–199.

CAMUS, G., and R. J. GAUTHERET. 1948a. Sur la transmission par greffage des propriétés tumorales des tissus de crown-gall. *C.r. Soc. Biol.*, Paris, **142**: 15–16.

———. 1948b. Nouvelles recherches sur le greffage de tissus normaux et tumoraux sur des fragments de racines de Scorsonère cultivés *in vitro. C.r. Soc. Biol.*, Paris, **142**: 769–771.

———. 1948c. Sur le caractère tumoral des tissus de Scorsonère ayant subi le phénomène d'accoutumance aux hétéro-auxines. *C.r. Acad. Sci.*, Paris, **226**: 744–745.

CAPLIN, S. M., and F. C. STEWARD. 1948. Effect of coconut milk on the growth of explants from carrot root. *Sci.* **108**: 655–657.

———. 1949. A technique for the controlled growth of excised plant tissue in liquid media under aseptic conditions. *Nature* **163**: 920–924.

CARPENTER, ESTHER. 1942. Differentiation of chick embryo thyroids in tissue culture. *J. Exp. Zool.* **89**: 407–422.

——. 1947. A mincing apparatus for the preparation of embryo extract for tissue culture. *Sci.* **106**: 621.

CARREL, A. 1912. On the permanent life of tissues outside of the organism. *J. Exp. Med.* **15**: 516–528.

——. 1913a. Concerning visceral organisms. *J. Exp. Med.* **18**: 155–161.

——. 1913b. Artificial activation of the growth *in vitro* of connective tissue. *J. Exp. Med.* **17**: 14–19.

——. 1913c. Neue Untersuchungen über das selbständige Leben der Gewebe und Organe. *Klin. Wochenschr.*, Berlin, **5**: 1097.

——. 1923a. Nouvelle technique pour la culture des tissus. *C.r. Soc. Biol.*, Paris, **89**: 1017–1019.

——. 1923b. A method for the physiological study of tissues *in vitro*. *J. Exp. Med.* **38**: 407–418.

——. 1924. Tissue culture and cell physiology. *Physiol. Rev.* **4**: 1–20.

——. 1934. Monocytes as an indicator of certain states of blood serum. *Sci.* **80**: 565–566.

CARREL, A., and L. E. BAKER. 1926. The chemical nature of substances required for cell multiplication. *J. Exp. Med.* **44**: 503–521.

CARREL, A., and C. A. LINDBERGH. 1938. *The culture of organs.* New York: Paul B. Hoeber, Inc.

CARRIÈRE, E. A. 1875. Greffes de Cucurbitacées. *Rev. Hort.* 1875: 14–16.

CHANG, M. C. 1948. Transplantation of fertilized rabbit ova: the effect on viability of age, *in vitro* storage period, and storage temperature. *Nature* **161**: 978–979.

——. 1950. Development and fate of transferred rabbit ova or blastocyst in relation to the ovulation time of recipient. *J. Exp. Zool.* **114**: 197–226.

CHANG, M. C., and G. PINCUS. 1951. Physiology of fertilization in mammals. *Physiol. Rev.* **31**: 1–26.

CHESTER, K. S. 1933. The problem of acquired physiological immunity in plants. *Quart. Rev. Biol.* **8**: 129–154, 275–324.

CHÈVREMONT, M. 1943. Recherches sur la production expérimentale de la transformation histiocytaire dans les cultures *in vitro*. *Arch. Biol.* **54**: 377–407.

CLARK-KENNEDY, A. E. 1929. *Stephen Hales, D.D., F.R.S. An eighteenth century biography.* London: Cambridge Univ. Press.

CONKLIN, E. G. 1940. Cell and protoplasm concepts: Historical account. *A.A.A.S. Publ.* **14**: 6–19.

CORNMAN, IVOR. 1947. (*Personal communication.*)

COSTERO, I., and C. M. POMERAT. 1951. Cultivation of neurons from the adult human cerebral and cerebellar cortex. *Am. J. Anat.* **89**: 405–468.

CURTIS, J. T. 1947. Undifferentiated growth of orchid embryos on media containing barbiturates. *Sci.* **105**: 128.

CURTIS, J. T., and M. A. NICHOL. 1948. Culture of proliferating orchid embryos *in vitro*. *Bull. Torrey Bot. Club* **75**: 358–373.

DANES, BETTY, and P. J. LEINFELDER. 1951. Cytological and respiratory effects of cyanide on tissue cultures. *J. Cell. Comp. Physiol.* **37**: 427–446.

DAVIDSON, F. F. 1950. The effects of auxins on the growth of marine algae. *Am. J. Bot.* **37**: 502–510.

DAWSON, RAY F. 1938. A method for the culture of excised plant parts. *Am. J. Bot.* **25**: 522–524.

Difco Manual of dehydrated culture media and reagents. 1953. 9th ed. Detroit: Difco Lab.

DOLJANSKI, L., and R. S. HOFFMAN. 1943. The growth activating effect of extract of adult tissue on fibroblast colonies *in vitro.* III, The cultivation for prolonged periods. *Growth* 7: 67–72.

DORMER, K. J., and H. E. STREET. 1949. The carbohydrate nutrition of tomato roots. *Ann. Bot.* 13: 199–217.

DREW, A. H. 1923. Growth and differentiation in tissue cultures. *Brit. J. Exp. Path.* 4: 46–52.

DUHAMEL DU MONCEAU, H. L. 1758. *La physique des arbres, où il est traité de l'anatomie des plantes et de l'économie végétale, pour servir d'introduction au traité complet des bois et des forêts; avec une dissertation sur l'utilité des méthodes de botanique.* (II vols.) Paris: Guérin et Delatour.

DUJARDIN, F. 1835. Recherches sur les organismes inférieurs. *Ann. Sci. nat. Zool.* 4: 343–376.

EARLE, W. R. 1939. Use of strip-shaped explants in tissue cultures. *Arch. Path.* 27: 88–94.

———. 1943a. Production of malignancy *in vitro.* I, Method of cleaning glassware. *J. Nat. Cancer Inst.* 4: 131–134.

———. 1943b. Production of malignancy *in vitro.* IV, The mouse fibroblast cultures and changes seen in the living cells. *J. Nat. Cancer Inst.* 4: 165–212.

EBELING, A. H. 1921a. Measurement of the growth of tissues *in vitro. J. Exp. Med.* 34: 231–243.

———. 1921b. Fibrin and serum as a culture medium. *J. Exp. Med.* 33: 641–646.

EHRENSVÄRD, G., A. FISCHER, and R. STJERNHOLM. 1949. Protein metabolism of tissue cells *in vitro.* VII, The chemical nature of some obligate factors of tissue cell nutrition. *Acta Physiol. Scand.* 18: 218–230.

EHRMANN, R. L., and G. O. GEY. 1953. The use of cell colonies on glass for evaluating nutrition and growth in roller tube cultures. *J. Nat. Cancer Inst.* 13: 1099–1122.

ENDERS, J. F. 1948. Propagation of viruses and Rickettsiae in tissue cultures. Chapter 5 in *Viral and Rickettsiae infections of man,* ed. by T. M. Rivers. Philadelphia: J. B. Lippincott Co.

EVANS, VIRGINIA J., and W. R. EARLE. 1947. The use of perforated cellophane for the growth of cells in tissue culture. *J. Nat. Cancer Inst.* 8: 103–119.

EVANS, VIRGINIA J., W. R. EARLE, K. K. SANFORD, J. E. SHANNON, and H. K. WALTZ. 1951. The preparation and handling of replicate tissue cultures for quantitative studies. *J. Nat. Cancer Inst.* 11: 907–927.

FAWCETT, D. W., and B. L. VALLEE. 1952. Studies on the separation of cell types in serosanguinous fluids, blood, and vaginal fluids by flotation on bovine plasma albumin. *J. Lab. & Clin. Med.* 39: 354–364.

FELL, H. B. 1928a. The development *in vitro* of the isolated otocyst of the embryonic fowl. *Arch. exp. Zellf.* 7: 69–81.

———. 1928b. Experiments on the differentiation *in vitro* of cartilage and bone. Part I. *Arch. exp. Zellf.* 7: 390–412.

———. 1931. Osteogenesis *in vitro.* *Arch. exp. Zellf.* 11: 245–252.

FELL, H. B., and E. MELLANBY. 1952. The effect of hypervitaminosis A on embryonic limb-bones cultivated *in vitro. J. Physiol.* **116:** 320–349.

———. 1953. Metaplasia produced in cultures of chick ectoderm by high Vitamin A. *J. Physiol.* **119:** 470–488.

FELL, H. B., and R. ROBISON. 1929. The growth, development and phosphatase activity of embryonic avian femora and limb-buds cultivated *in vitro. Biochem. J.* **23:** 767–784.

FELLER, A. E., J. F. ENDERS, and T. H. WELLER. 1940. The prolonged coexistence of vaccinia virus in high titre and living cells in roller tube cultures of chick embryonic tissues. *J. Exp. Med.* **72:** 367–380.

FIEDLER, H. 1936. Entwicklungs- und reizphysiologische Untersuchungen an Kulturen isolierter Wurzelspitzen. *Ztschz. Bot.* **30:** 385–436.

FIFE, J. M., and V. L. FRAMPTON. 1936. The *p*H gradient extending from the phloem into the parenchyma of the sugar beet and its relation to the feeding habits of *Eutettix tenellus. J. Agric. Res.* **53:** 581–593.

FILATOW, D. 1925. Ersatz des linsenbildenden Epithels von *Rana esculenta* durch Bauchepithel von *Bufo vulgaris. Arch. entw.-mech. Org.* **105:** 475–482.

FIROR, W. M., and G. O. GEY. 1945. Observations on the conversion of normal into malignant cells. *Ann. Surg.* **121:** 700–703.

FISCHER, A. 1922. Cultures of organized tissues. *J. Exp. Med.* **36:** 393–397.

———. 1925. Sur la transformation *in vitro* des gros leucocytes mononucléaires en fibroblastes. *C.r. Soc. Biol.,* Paris, **92:** 109–112.

———. 1926. Umwandlung von Fibroblasten zu Makrophagen *in vitro. Arch. exp. Zellf.* **3:** 345–352.

———. 1930. *Gewebezüchtung.* 3d ed. Munich: Müller und Steinicke.

———. 1941a. The nature of the growth promoting substances in embryonic tissue juice. *Acta Physiol. Scand.* **3:** 54–70.

———. 1941b. Die bedeutung der Aminosäuren für die Gewebezellen *in vitro. Acta Physiol. Scand.* **2:** 145–188.

———. 1948. Amino-acid metabolism of tissue cells *in vitro. Biochem. J.* **43:** 491–497.

FISCHER, A., and F. DEMUTH. 1928. Eiweissabbauprodukte als wachstumsfördernde Substanzen. *Arch. exp. Zellf.* **5:** 131–142.

FISCHER, A., T. ASTRUP, G. EHRENSVÄRD, and V. OEHLENSCHLÄGER. 1948. Growth of animal tissue cells in artificial media. *Proc. Soc. Exp. Biol. Med.* **67:** 40–46.

FRÉDÉRIC, J. 1951. La transformation histiocytaire des cellules hépatiques cultivées "in vitro" et son déterminisme. *Rev. Hématol.* **6:** 423–447.

GAILLARD, P. J. 1948. Growth, differentiation and function of explants of some endocrine glands. *Symp., Soc. Exp. Biol.* **2:** 139–145.

GAUTHERET, R. J. 1934. Culture du tissu cambial. *C.r. Acad. Sci.,* Paris, **198:** 2195–2196.

———. 1935. Recherches sur la culture des tissus végétaux: Essais de culture de quelques tissus méristématiques. Thèse, Univ. de Paris. 279 pp.

———. 1937. Nouvelles recherches sur la culture du tissu cambial. *C.r. Acad. Sci.,* Paris, **205:** 572–574.

———. 1938a. Sur le repiquage des cultures de tissu cambial de *Salix capraea. C.r. Acad. Sci.,* Paris, **206:** 125–127.

GAUTHERET, R. J. 1938b. Recherches sur la culture de fragments de tubercules de carotte. *C.r. Acad. Sci.*, Paris, **206**: 457–459.

———. 1939. Sur la possibilité de réaliser la culture indéfinie des tissus de tubercules de carotte. *C.r. Acad. Sci.*, Paris, **208**: 118–120.

———. 1940. Recherches sur le bourgeonnement du tissu cambial d'*Ulmus campestris* cultivé *in vitro*. *C.r. Acad. Sci.*, Paris, **210**: 632–634.

———. 1942a. *Manuel technique de culture des tissus végétaux.* Préface de Alexis Carrel. Paris: Masson et Cie, 172 pp., 95 figs.

———. 1942b. Hétéro-auxines et cultures de tissus végétaux. *Bull. Soc. Chim. Biol.* **24**: 13–47.

———. 1946. Comparaison entre l'action de l'acide indole-acétique et celle du *Phytomonas tumefaciens* sur la croissance des tissus végétaux. *C.r. Soc. Biol.*, Paris, **140**: 169–171.

———. 1947a. Sur les besoins en hétéro-auxine des cultures de tissus de quelques végétaux. *C.r. Soc. Biol.*, Paris, **141**: 627–629.

———. 1947b. Action de l'acide indole-acétique sur le développement des tissus normaux et des tissus de crown-gall de topinambour cultivés *in vitro*. *C.r. Acad. Sci.*, Paris, **224**: 1728–1730.

———. 1948a. Sur la culture de trois types de tissus de Scorsonère: tissus normaux, tissus de Crown-Gall et tissus accoutumés a l'hétéro-auxine. *C.r. Acad. Sci.*, Paris, **226**: 270–271.

———. 1948b. La culture des tissus végétaux. *Endeavour* 7 (April, 1948).

———. 1950. Remarques sur les besoins nutritifs des cultures de tissus de *Salix capraea*. *C.r. Soc. Biol.*, Paris, **144**: 173–174.

GEY, G. O. 1933. An improved technic for massive tissue culture. *Am. J. Cancer* **17**: 752–756.

GEY, G. O., and F. BANG. 1951. Viruses and cells—a study in tissue culture applications. I, Cells involved, availability and susceptibility. II, Effect of several viruses on cell types and the amount of virus produced. *Trans. N.Y. Acad. Sci.* **14**: 15–24.

GEY, G. O., and M. K. GEY. 1936. The maintenance of human normal cells and tumor cells in continuous culture. I, Preliminary report: Cultivation of mesoblastic tumors and normal tissue and notes on methods of cultivation. *Am. J. Cancer* **27**: 45–76.

GEY, G. O., G. E. SEEGAR, and L. M. HELLMAN. 1938. The production of a gonadotrophic substance (prolan) by placental cells in tissue culture. *Sci.* **88**: 306–307.

GILCHRIST, F. G. 1928. The effect of a horizontal temperature gradient on the development of the egg of the Urodele, *Triturus torosus*. *Physiol. Zool.* **1**: 231–268.

GIOELLI, F. 1938a. Morfologia, istologia, fisiologia e fisiopatologia di meristemi secondari *in vitro*. *Atti Accad. Sci.*, Ferrara, **16**: 1–87.

———. 1938b. Comportamento delle culture *in vitro* di meristemi cambiali in rapporto all' andamento stagionale. *Atti Accad. Sci.*, Ferrara, **16**: 1–9.

Goebel, K. 1908. *Einleitung in die experimentelle Morphologie der Pflanzen.* Leipzig and Berlin: Teubner Verlag. 260 pp.

GOETHE, JOHANN WOLFGANG VON. 1882. *Faust, Erster Theil* (1808), *Zweiter Theil* (1832), in *Goethes Werke*, ed. by H. Düntzer. Leipzig: Deutsche Verlagsanstalt. IV vols.

GREW, NEHEMIAH. 1682. *The anatomy of plants, with an idea of a philosophical history of plants, and several other lectures, read before the Royal Society.* London: Rawlins.

HABERLANDT, G. 1902. Kulturversuche mit isolierten Pflanzenzellen. *Sitzungsber. Akad. Wiss. Wien, Math.-naturw. Kl.* 111: 69–92.

HACKETT, D. P., and K. THIMANN. 1950. The action of inhibitors on water uptake by potato tissue. *Plant Physiol.* 25: 648–652.

HANKS, J. H. 1947. A study of the bacilli in tissue culture of lepromata in serum media. *Internat. J. Leprosy* 15: 21–30.

——. 1948. The longevity of chick tissue cultures without renewal of the medium. *J. Cell. Comp. Physiol.* 31: 235–260.

——. 1952. *Outline of the Cooperstown tissue culture course.* (Mimeographed.)

HARRIS, M. 1943. The compatibility of rat and mouse cells in mixed tissue cultures. *Anat. Rec.* 87: 107–117.

——. 1952a. The use of dialyzed media for studies in cell nutrition. *J. Cell. Comp. Physiol.* 40: 279–302.

——. 1952b. Growth factors in alcoholic extracts of chick embryos. *Growth* 16: 215–230.

HARRISON, R. G. 1904. Experimentelle Untersuchungen über die Entwicklung der Sinnesorgane der Seitenlinie bei den Amphibien. *Arch. mikr. Anat.* 63: 35–149.

——. 1907. Observations on the living developing nerve fiber. *Proc. Soc. Exp. Biol. Med.* 4: 140–143.

——. 1908. Embryonic transplantation and development of the nervous system. *Anat. Rec.* 2: 385–410.

——. 1910. The outgrowth of the nerve fiber as a mode of protoplasmic movement. *J. Exp. Zool.* 9: 787–848.

——. 1912. The cultivation of tissues in extraneous media as a method of morphogenetic study. *Anat. Rec.* 6: 181–193.

——. 1928. On the status and significance of tissue culture. *Arch. exp. Zellf.* 6: 4–27.

HELLER, R. 1949. Sur l'emploi de papier filtre sans cendres comme support pour les cultures de tissus végétaux. *C.r. Soc. Biol.,* Paris, 143: 335–337.

HELLER, R., and R. J. GAUTHERET. 1947. Sur l'emploi d'un ruban de verre comme support pour les cultures de tissus végétaux. *C.r. Soc. Biol.,* Paris, 141: 662–665.

HENDERSON, J. H. M., and F. F. STAUFFER. 1944. The influence of some respiratory inhibitors and intermediates on growth and respiration of excised tomato roots. *Am. J. Bot.* 31: 528–535.

HILDEBRANDT, A. C., and A. J. RIKER. 1949. The influence of various carbon compounds on the growth of marigold, paris daisy, periwinkle, sunflower and tobacco tissue *in vitro. Am. J. Bot.* 36: 74–85.

——. 1953. Influence of concentrations of sugars and polysaccharides on callus tissue growth *in vitro. Am. J. Bot.* 40: 66–76.

HILDEBRANDT, A. C., A. J. RIKER, and B. M. DUGGAR. 1946. The influence of the composition of the medium on growth *in vitro* of excised tobacco and sunflower tissue cultures. *Am. J. Bot.* 33: 591–597.

HOAGLAND, D. R., and W. C. SNYDER. 1933. Nutrition of strawberry plant under controlled conditions. *Proc. Am. Soc. Hort. Sci.* **30**: 288–294.

HOFFMAN, R. S., and L. DOLJANSKI. 1939. The growth activating effect of extracts of adult tissue on fibroblast colonies *in vitro*. Experiments with chicken heart extracts. *Growth* **3**: 61–71.

HOFFMAN, R. S., J. DINGWALL, and W. ANDRUS. 1951. Growth effects on chick fibroblast cultures of fractions of adult and embryonic tissue extracts following differential centrifugation. *Sci.* **113**: 268–269.

HOLTFRETER, J. 1929. Über die Aufzucht isolierter Teile des Amphibien-keimes. I, Methode einer Gewebezüchtung *in vivo*. *Arch. Entw.-mech. Org.* **117**: 421–510.

–––. 1931. Über die Aufzucht isolierter Teile des Amphibienkeimes. II, Züchtung von Keimen und Keimteilen in Salzlösung. *Arch. Entw.-mech. Org.* **124**: 404–466.

HOOKE, ROBERT. 1667. *Micrographia: or some physiological descriptions of minute bodies made by magnifying glasses with observations and inquiries thereupon.* 1665 ed. London: John Martyn and James Allestry. John Martyn—Printer to the Royal Society. (Pritzel No. 4198.)

HUXLEY, J. S. 1927. Modification of development by means of temperature gradients. *Arch. Entw.-mech. Org.* **112**: 480–516.

JOLLY, J. 1903. Sur la durée de la vie et de la multiplication des cellules animales en dehors de l'organisme. *C.r. Soc. Biol.,* Paris, **55**: 1266–1268.

JONES, G., E. SEEGAR, G. O. GEY, and M. K. GEY. 1942. Hormone production by placental cells maintained in continuous cultures. *Bull. Johns Hopkins Hosp.* **72**: 26–38.

KNOP, W. 1865. Quantitative Untersuchungen über den Ernährungsprozess der Pflanzen. *Landw. Versuchs-Stat.* **7**: 93–107.

–––. 1884. Bereitung einer conzentrierten Nährstofflösung für Pflanzen. *Landw. Versuchs-Stat.* **30**: 292–294.

KOTTE, W. 1922. Kulturversuche mit isolierten Wurzelspitzen. *Beitr. allg. Bot.* **2**: 413–434.

KULESCHA, ZOJA, and R. J. GAUTHERET. 1948. Sur l'élaboration de sub-stances de croissance par trois types de cultures de tissus de Scorsonère: cultures normales, cultures de Crown-Gall et cultures accoutumées à l'hétéro-auxine. *C.r. Acad. Sci.,* Paris, **227**: 292–294.

KUTSKY, R. J. 1953. Stimulating effect of nucleoprotein fraction of chick embryo extract on homologous heart fibroblasts. *Proc. Soc. Exp. Biol. Med.* **83**: 390–395.

LASER, H. 1933. Flächengrösse und Wachtum von Gewebekulturen. *Ztschr. f. Krebsforsch.* **39**: 384–390.

LEWIS, MARGARET R. 1928. A simple method of drawing blood from the heart of a fowl. *Arch. exp. Zellf.* **7**: 82–86.

LEWIS, MARGARET R., and W. H. LEWIS. 1911a. The cultivation of tissues from chick embryos in solutions of NaCl, $CaCl_2$, KCl, and $NaHCO_3$. *Anat. Rec.* **5**: 277–293.

–––. 1911b. The growth of embryonic chicken tissues in artificial media, agar and bouillon. *Bull. Johns Hopkins Hosp.* **22**: 126–127.

–––. 1912a. The cultivation of sympathetic nerves from the intestine of chicken embryos in saline solutions. *Anat. Rec.* **6**: 7–32.

———. 1912b. The cultivation of chicken tissues in media of known chemical constitution. *Anat. Rec.* **6**: 207–211.

———. 1926. Transformation of mononuclear blood-cells into macrophages, epithelioid cells, and giant cells in hanging-drop blood-cultures from lower vertebrates. *Carnegie Inst. Wash., Publ. No. 363, Contrib. to Embryol.* **18**: 95–120.

LEWIS, W. H. 1934. Rat malignant cells in roller tube cultures and some results. *Carnegie Inst. Wash., Publ. No. 459, Contrib. to Embryol.* **25**: 161–172.

LEWIS, W. H., and ELSIE S. WRIGHT. 1935. On the early development of the mouse egg. *Carnegie Inst. Wash., Publ. No. 459, Contrib. to Embryol.* **148**: 113–144.

LI, C. R., and T. M. RIVERS. 1930. Cultivation of vaccine virus. *J. Exp. Med.* **52**: 465–470.

LIMASSET, P., and R. J. GAUTHERET. 1950. Sur le caractère tumoral des tissus de tabac ayant subi le phénomène d'accoutumance aux hétéroauxines. *C.r. Acad. Sci.*, Paris, **230**: 2043–2045.

LIPMANN, F. 1932. Versuche zur Methodik der Messung des Zuwachses *in vitro* wachsender Gewebe durch Messung des Umsatzanstiegs. *Biochem. Ztschr.* **244**: 177–186.

———. 1933. Stoffwechselversuche an Gewebekulturen, insbesondere über die Rolle der Glykolyse im Stoffwechsel embryonaler Zellen. *Biochem. Ztschr.* **261**: 157–164.

LIPMANN, F., and A. FISCHER. 1932. Proliferationsgrösse von Gewebezellen *in vitro* und Stoffumsatz. *Biochem. Ztschr.* **244**: 187–189.

LJUNGGREN, C. A. 1897–98. Von der Fähigkeit des Hautepithels, ausserhalb des Organismus sein Leben zu behalten, mit Berüchsichtigung der Transplantation. *Deutsch. Ztschr. f. Chir.* **47**: 608–615.

LOCKE, F. S. 1895. Artificial fluids as uninjurious as possible to animal tissue. *Boston Med. & Surg. J.* **134**: 173. (Reprinted in *J. Boston Soc. Med. Sci.* **1**(1): 2–3, 1896.)

———. 1901. Die Wirkung der Metalle des Blutplasmas und verschiedener Zucker auf das isolierte Säugethierherz. *Centr. Physiol.* **14**: 670.

LOEB, L. 1902. On the growth of epithelium in agar and blood-serum in the living body. *J. Med. Res.* **8**: 109–115.

LOEWENBERG, J. R., and F. SKOOG. 1952. Pine tissue cultures. *Physiol. Plantarum* **5**: 33–36.

LÖWENSTADT, H. 1925. Einige neue Hilfsmittel zur Angebung von Gewebekulturen. *Arch. exp. Zellf.* **1**: 251–256.

MADDEN, S. C., and G. H. WHIPPLE. 1940. Plasma proteins: their source, production and utilization. *Physiol. Rev.* **20**: 194–217.

MADDEN, S. C., J. R. CARTER, A. A. KATTUS, JR., L. L. MILLER, and G. H. WHIPPLE. 1943. Ten amino-acids essential for plasma protein production effective orally or intravenously. *J. Exp. Med.* **77**: 277–295.

MAITLAND, H. B., and M. C. MAITLAND. 1928. Cultivation of vaccinia virus without tissue culture. *Lancet* **2**: 596–597.

MARTINOVICH, P. N. 1938. The development *in vitro* of the mammalian gonad, ovary and ovogenesis. *Proc. Roy. Soc.*, London, **B 125**: 232–249.

———. 1950. Anterior pituitary explants of infantile rats grafted in the anterior eye chamber of hypophysectomized hosts. *Nature* **165**: 33–35.

212   THE CULTIVATION OF CELLS

Maximow, A. 1925. Tissue cultures of young mammalian embryos. *Carnegie Inst. Wash., Publ. No. 361, Contrib. to Embryol.* **16**: 47–113.

Meier, R. 1931. Zur Methodik der Stoffwechseluntersuchungen an Gewebekulturen. II, Gewichtsbestimmung an einzelnen Gewebekulturen. Gewichtszunahme und Flächenzunahme. Vorläufige Mitteilung. *Biochem. Ztschr.* **231**: 253–259.

Molliard, M. 1921. Sur le développement des plantules fragmentées. *C.r. Soc. Biol.,* Paris, **84**: 770–772.

Morel, G. 1944a. Le développement du mildiou sur les tissus de vigne cultivés *in vitro. C.r. Acad. Sci.,* Paris, **218**: 50–52.

––––. 1944b. Sur la possibilité de réaliser la culture indéfinie des tissus de vigne. *C.r. Acad. Sci.,* Paris, **219**: 36–37.

––––. 1945. Isolement des cultures pures de parenchyme de Vigne. *C.r. Acad. Sci.,* Paris, **221**: 78–80.

––––. 1946. Action de l'acide pantothénique sur la croissance des tissus d'Aubépine cultivés *in vitro. C.r. Acad. Sci.,* Paris, **223**: 166–168.

––––. 1948. Recherches sur la culture associée de parasites obligatoires et de tissus végétaux. *Ann. Epiphyties* **14**: 123–234.

Morel, G., and R. H. Wetmore. 1951. Fern callus tissue cultures. *Am. J. Bot.* **38**: 141–143.

Morgan, J. F., H. J. Morton, and R. C. Parker. 1950. Nutrition of animal cells in tissue culture. I, Initial studies on a synthetic medium. *Proc. Soc. Exp. Biol. Med.* **73**: 1–8.

Morgan, J. F., and R. C. Parker. 1952. Interrelationships between cobalt and aminoacids in tissue culture. *Arch. Biochem. and Biophys.* **38**: 267–274.

Morton, Helen J., J. F. Morgan and R. C. Parker. 1950. Nutrition of animal cells in tissue culture. II, Use of Tweens in synthetic feeding mixtures. *Proc. Soc. Exp. Biol. Med.* **74**: 22–26.

Murneek, A. E. 1935. Physiological rôle of asparagine and related substances in nitrogen metabolism of plants. *Plant Physiol.* **10**: 447–464.

Murray, Margaret R., and A. P. Stout. 1942. Demonstration of the formation of reticulin by Schwannian tumor cells *in vitro. Am. J. Path.* **18**: 585–593.

––––. 1947. Distinctive characteristics of the sympathicoblastoma cultivated *in vitro.* A method for prompt diagnosis. *Am. J. Path.* **23**: 429–441.

Naylor, E. E. 1931. The morphology of regeneration of *Bryophyllum calycinum. Am. J. Bot.* **19**: 32–40.

Nickell, L. G. 1951. Embryo culture of weeping crabapple. *Proc. Am. Soc. Hort. Sci.* **57**: 401–405.

Nitsch, J. 1949a. Culture of fruits *in vitro. Sci.* **110**: 499.

––––. 1949b. Obtention de fruits charnus en culture *in vitro. C.r. Acad. Sci.,* Paris, **229**: 445–446.

––––. 1951. Growth and development *in vitro* of excised ovaries. *Am. J. Bot.* **38**: 566–577.

Nobécourt, P. 1937. Cultures en série de tissus végétaux sur milieu artificiel. *C.r. Acad. Sci.,* Paris, **205**: 521–523.

––––. 1939a. Sur la pérennité et l'augmentation de volume des cultures de tissus végétaux. *C.r. Soc. Biol.,* Paris, **130**: 1270.

———. 1939b. Sur les radicelles naissant des cultures de tissus du tubercule de carotte. *C.r. Soc. Biol.*, Paris, **130**: 1271.

NOBÉCOURT, P., and LUCIE KÖFLER. 1945. Culture de tissus de tige de rosier. *C.r. Acad. Sci.*, Paris, **221**: 53–54.

NORTHCRAFT, R. D. 1951. The use of oxalate to produce free-living cells from carrot tissue cultures. *Sci.* **113**: 407–408.

VAN OVERBEEK, J. 1939. Evidence for auxin production in isolated roots growing *in vitro*. *Bot. Gaz.* **101**: 450–456.

VAN OVERBEEK, J., M. E. CONKLIN, and A. F. BLAKESLEE. 1941. Factors in coconut milk essential for growth and development of very young *Datura* embryos. *Sci.* **94**: 350–351.

———. 1942. Cultivation *in vitro* of small *Datura* embryos. *Am. J. Bot.* **29**: 472–477.

PAINTER, J. T., C. M. POMERAT, and D. EZELL. 1949. The effect of substances known to influence the activity of the nervous system on fiber outgrowths from living embryonic chick spinal cords. *Texas Rep. Biol. Med.* **7**: 417–455.

PARKER, R. C. 1931. Structural and functional variations of fibroblasts in pure cultures. *Sci.* **73**: 401–402.

———. 1932a. The races that constitute the group of common fibroblasts. I, The effect of blood plasma. *J. Exp. Med.* **55**: 713–734.

———. 1932b. The functional characteristics of nine races of fibroblasts. *Sci.* **76**: 219–220.

———. 1950. *Methods of tissue culture.* 2d ed. New York: Paul B. Hoeber, Inc.

PARSHLEY, M. S., and H. S. SIMMS. 1946. Conditions favoring the growth of adult skin epithelium *in vitro*. *Anat. Rec.* **94**: 42–43.

PLANTEFOL, L. 1938. Sur les échanges respiratoires des tissus végétaux en culture. *C.r. Acad. Sci.*, Paris, **207**: 1121–1123.

PLANTEFOL, L., and R. J. GAUTHERET. 1939. Le glucose et la respiration des cultures de tissus végétaux. *C.r. Acad. Sci.*, Paris, **208**: 927–929.

———. 1941. Sur l'intensité des échanges respiratoires des tissus végétaux en culture: tissu primitif et tissu néoformé. *C.r. Acad. Sci.*, Paris, **213**: 627–629.

POMERAT, C. M. (ed.). 1951. Tissue culture methods. Section IV in *Methods of medical research*, Vol. 4. Chicago: Year Book Publishers, Inc.

———. 1951. Perfusion chamber. In *Methods of medical research*, Vol. 4. Chicago: Year Book Publishers, Inc., pp. 275–277.

———. 1952. Motion picture studies of living papilloma of the breast and breast cancer. 5th Symposium on Cancer Research. *Texas Rep. Biol. Med.* **10**: 217–227.

PORTER, K. R. 1947. The culture of tissue cells in clots formed from purified bovine fibrinogen and thrombin. *Proc. Soc. Exp. Biol. Med.* **65**: 309–314.

PORTER, K. R., and H. P. THOMPSON. 1947. Some morphological features of cultured rat sarcoma cells as revealed by the electron microscope. *Cancer Res.* **7**: 431–438.

PORTER, K. R., A. CLAUDE, and E. F. FULLAM. 1945. A study of tissue culture cells by electron microscopy. *J. Exp. Med.* **81**: 233–246.

PRICE, W. C. 1940. Generalized defense reactions in plants. *Am. Nat.* **74:** 117–128.

PRIESTLEY, J. H. 1928. The meristematic tissue of the plant. *Biol. Rev.* **3:** 1–20.

RANDOLPH, L. F. 1945. Embryo culture of Iris seed. *Bull. Am. Iris Soc.* **97:** 33–45.

RECHINGER, C. 1893. Untersuchungen über die Grenzen der Teilbarkeit im Pflanzenreich. *Abh. zool.-bot. Ges.*, Wien, **43:** 310–334.

RIKER, A. J., and A. E. GUTSCHE. 1948. The growth of sunflower tissue *in vitro* on synthetic media with various organic and inorganic sources of nitrogen. *Am. J. Bot.* **35:** 227–238.

RINGER, S. 1886. Further experiments regarding the influence of lime, potassium and other salts on muscular tissue. *J. Physiol.* **7:** 291–308.

RIVERS, T. M., E. HAAGEN, and R. S. MUCKENFUSS. 1929. A study of vaccinal immunity in tissue cultures. *J. Exp. Med.* **50:** 673–685.

ROBBINS, F. C., and J. F. ENDERS. 1950. Tissue culture techniques in study of animal viruses. *Am. J. Med. Sci.* **220:** 316–338.

ROBBINS, W. J. 1922a. Cultivation of excised root tips and stem tips under sterile conditions. *Bot. Gaz.* **73:** 376–390.

———. 1922b. Effect of autolyzed yeast and peptone on growth of excised corn root tips in the dark. *Bot. Gaz.* **74:** 59–79.

ROBBINS, W. J., and MARY A. BARTLEY. 1937. Vitamin B$_1$ and the growth of excised tomato roots. *Sci.* **85:** 246–247.

ROBBINS, W. J., and W. E. MANEVAL. 1923. Further experiments on growth of excised root tips under sterile conditions. *Bot. Gaz.* **76:** 274–287.

———. 1924. Effect of light on growth of excised root tips under sterile conditions. *Bot. Gaz.* **78:** 424–432.

ROBBINS, W. J., and MARY B. SCHMIDT. 1938. Growth of excised roots of the tomato. *Bot. Gaz.* **99:** 671–728.

———. 1939a. Further experiments on excised tomato roots. *Am. J. Bot.* **26:** 149–159.

———. 1939b. Growth of excised tomato roots in a synthetic solution. *Bull. Torrey Bot. Club* **66:** 193–200.

———. 1939c. Vitamin B$_6$, a growth substance for excised tomato roots. *Proc. Nat. Acad. Sci.*, Wash., **25:** 1–3.

ROBBINS, W. J., VIRGINIA B. WHITE, J. E. McCLARY, and MARY A. BARTLEY. 1936. The importance of ash elements in the cultivation of excised root tips. *Proc. Nat. Acad. Sci.*, Wash., **22:** 636–639.

DEROPP, R. S. 1947. The response of normal plant tissues and of crown-gall tumor tissues to synthetic growth hormones. *Am. J. Bot.* **34:** 53–62.

———. 1948. The interaction of normal and crown-gall tumor tissue in *in vitro* grafts. *Am. J. Bot.* **35:** 372–377.

ROSE, W. C. 1932. The amino acids in nutrition. *Yale J. Biol. & Med.* **4:** 519–536.

ROSENE, H. F. 1941. Comparison of rates of water intake in contiguous regions of intact and isolated roots. *Plant Physiol.* **16:** 19–38.

ROSENE, H. F., and E. J. LUND. 1935. Linkage between output of electric energy by polar tissues and cell oxidation. *Plant Physiol.* **10:** 27–47.

Roux, Wilhelm. 1885. Beiträge zur Entwicklungsmechanik des Embryo. *Ztschr. Biol.* **21:** 411–526.

Sanford, Katherine K., W. R. Earle, V. J. Evans, H. K. Waltz, and J. E. Shannon. 1951. The measurement of proliferation in tissue cultures by enumeration of cell nuclei. *J. Nat. Cancer Inst.* **11:** 773–795.

Sanford, Katherine K., W. R. Earle, and G. D. Likely. 1948. The growth *in vitro* of single isolated tissue cells. *J. Nat. Cancer Inst.* **9:** 229–246.

Schleiden, M. J. 1838. Beiträge zur Phytogenesis. *Arch. Anat., Physiol. u. wiss. Med.* (J. Müller) 1838: 137–176.

Schmucker, T. 1929. Isolierte Gewebe und Zellen von Blütenpflanzen. *Planta* **9:** 339–340.

Schwann, Th. 1839. *Mikroskopische Untersuchungen über die Übereinstimmung in der Struktur und dem Wachstume der Tiere und Pflanzen.* Leipzig: W. Engelmann, Nr. 176, Ostwalds Klassiker der exakten Wissenschaften, 1910.

Sharp, L. W. 1926. *An introduction to cytology.* 2d ed. New York: McGraw-Hill Book Co., Inc.

Shaw, D. T., L. C. Kingsland, and A. M. Brues. 1940. A roller bottle tissue culture system. *Sci.* **91:** 148–149.

Skoog, F. 1951. Chemical control of growth and organ formation in plant tissues. *Année biol.* **26:** 545–562.

Skoog, F., and C. Tsui. 1948. Chemical control of growth and bud formation in tobacco stem segments and callus cultured *in vitro*. *Am. J. Bot.* **35:** 782–787.

Spemann, H. 1936. *Experimentelle Beiträge zu einer Theorie der Entwicklung.* Berlin: J. Springer.

Stanley, W. M. 1938. Aucuba mosaic virus protein isolated from diseased, excised tomato roots grown *in vitro*. *J. Biol. Chem.* **126:** 125–131.

Steward, F. C., and S. M. Caplin. 1951. A tissue culture from potato tuber: the synergistic action of 2,4-D and of coconut milk. *Sci.* **113:** 518–520.

Steward, F. C., and J. C. Martin. 1937. The distribution and physiology of *Valonia* at the dry Tortugas with special reference to the problem of salt accumulation in plants. *Carnegie Inst. Wash., Publ. No. 475,* pp. 87–170.

Stone, H. B., J. C. Owings, and G. O. Gey. 1934a. Transplantation of living grafts of thyroid and parathyroid glands. *Ann. Surg.* 1934: 262–277.

———. 1934b. Living grafts of endocrine glands. *Am. J. Surg.* **24:** 386–392.

Street, H. E. 1950. The role of high-energy phosphate bonds in biosynthesis. *Sci. Progress* **38:** 43–66.

Street, H. E., and J. S. Lowe. 1950. The carbohydrate nutrition of tomato roots. II, The mechanism of sucrose absorption by excised roots. *Ann. Bot.* **14:** 307–329.

Street, H. E., and S. M. McGregor. 1952. The carbohydrate nutrition of tomato roots. III, The effects of external sucrose concentration on the growth and anatomy of excised roots. *Ann. Bot.* **16:** 185–205.

Theophrastus. Ca. 320 b.c. *Enquiry into plants.* Tr. by Sir Arthur Hort. New York: G. P. Putnam's Sons, Loeb Classical Library, 1916.

216 THE CULTIVATION OF CELLS

Trelease, S., and H. M. Trelease. 1933. Physiologically balanced culture solutions with stable hydrogen-ion concentration. *Sci.* **78**: 438–439.

Tukey, H. B. 1933. Artificial culture of sweet cherry embryos. *J. Hered.* **24**: 7–12.

———. 1934. Artificial culture methods for isolated embryos of deciduous fruits. *Am. Soc. Hort. Sci.* **32**: 313–322.

Tyrode, M. V. 1910. The mode of action of some purgative salts. *Arch. Internat. Pharmacodyn.* **20**: 205–223.

Underwood, W. B. 1941. *A textbook of sterilization.* Erie, Pa.: Am. Sterilizer Co.

Uspenski, E. E., and W. J. Uspenskaia. 1925. Reinkultur und ungeschlechtliche fortpflanzung der *Volvox minor* und *Volvox globator* in einer synthetischen Nährlösung. *Ztschr. Bot.* **17**: 273–308.

Verworn, M. 1895. *Allgemeine Physiologie. Ein Grundriss der Lehre vom Leben.* Jena: Fischer.

Vickery, H. B., G. W. Pucher, and H. E. Clark. 1936. Glutamine metabolism of the beet. *Plant Physiol.* **11**: 413–420.

Vickery, H. B., G. W. Pucher, A. J. Wakeman, and C. L. Leavenworth. 1937. Chemical investigations of the tobacco plant. VI, Chemical changes that occur in leaves during culture in light and darkness. *Conn. Agr. Exp. Sta. Bull.* 399, pp. 757–832.

Virchow, R. 1858. *Die Cellularpathologie in ihrer Begründung auf physiologische und pathologische Gewebelehre.* Berlin.

Vöchting, H. 1878, 1884. *Ueber Organbildung im Pflanzenreich.* I. Th. 1878; II. Th. 1884. Bonn.

———. 1892. *Über Transplantation am Pflanzenkörper. Untersuchungen zur Physiologie und Pathologie.* Tübingen: H. Laupp.

———. 1894. Ueber die durch Pfropfen herbeigeführte Symbiose des *Helianthus tuberosus* und *Helianthus annuus. Sitzngsber. K. Preuss Akad. Wiss.,* Berlin, 1894: 705–721.

Vogelaar, J. P. M., and Eleanor Erlichman. 1933. A feeding solution for cultures of human fibroblasts. *Am. J. Cancer* **18**: 28–38.

———. 1939. Contributions to tissue culture technic. *Am. J. Cancer* **35**: 510–520.

Vogt, W. 1932. Einige Ergebnisse aus Versuchen mit halbseitiger Temperaturhemmung am Amphibienkeim. *Rev. suisse Zool.* **39**: 309–324.

Warburg, O., and F. Kubowitz. 1927. Stoffwechsel wachsender Zellen (Fibroblasten, Herz, Chorion). *Biochem. Ztschr.* **189**: 242–248.

Waymouth, Charity. 1947. Proteins with growth-promoting action on tissue cells *in vitro. Proc. Soc. Exp. Biol. Med.* **64**: 25–26.

———. 1950. A new type of hexagonal roller tube for growing multiple tissue cultures. *J. Physiol.* **111**: 54P–55P.

Weiss, L. P., and D. W. Fawcett. 1953. Cytochemical observations on chicken monocytes, macrophages and giant cells in tissue culture. *J. Histochem. & Cytochem.* **1**: 47–65.

Weiss, P. 1929. Erzwingung elementarer Strukturverschiedenheiten am *in vitro* wachsenden Gewebe. (Die Wirkung mechanischer Spannung auf Richtung und Intensität des Gewebewachstums und ihre Analyse.) *Arch. Entw. mech. Org.* **116**: 438–554.

WELLER, T. H., and J. F. ENDERS. 1948. Production of hemagglutinin by mumps and influenza A viruses in suspended cell tissue cultures. *Proc. Soc. Exp. Biol. Med.* **69**: 124–128.

WELLER, T. H. 1953. The application of tissue culture methods to the study of poliomyelitis. *N.E. J. of Med* **249**: 186–195.

WETMORE, R. H., and G. MOREL. 1951a. Sur la culture *in vitro* de prothalle de *Lycopodium cernuum*. *C.r. Acad. Sci.*, Paris, **233**: 323–324.

——. 1951b. Sur la culture du gamétophyte de Sélaginelle. *C.r. Acad. Sci.*, Paris, **223**: 430–431.

WHITE, P. R. 1928. Studies on the banana. An investigation of the floral morphology and cytology of certain types of the genus *Musa* L. *Ztschr. f. Zellf. und mikr. Anat.* **7**: 673–733.

——. 1931. Plant tissue cultures. The history and present status of the problem. *Arch. exp. Zellf.* **10**: 501–518.

——. 1932a. Plant tissue cultures. A preliminary report of results obtained in the culturing of certain plant meristems. *Arch. exp. Zellf.* **12**: 602–620.

——. 1932b. Influence of some environmental conditions on the growth of excised root tips of wheat seedlings in liquid media. *Plant Physiol.* **7**: 613–628.

——. 1933a. Plant tissue cultures. Results of preliminary experiments on the culturing of isolated stem-tips of *Stellaria media*. *Protoplasma* **19**: 97–116.

——. 1933b. Concentrations of inorganic ions as related to growth of excised root-tips of wheat seedlings. *Plant Physiol.* **8**: 489–508.

——. 1934a. Potentially unlimited growth of excised tomato root tips in a liquid medium. *Plant Physiol.* **9**: 585–600.

——. 1934b. Multiplication of the viruses of tobacco and aucuba mosaic in growing excised tomato root tips. *Phytopath.* **24**: 1003–1011.

——. 1937a. Separation from yeast of materials essential for growth of excised tomato roots. *Plant Physiol.* **12**: 777–791.

——. 1937b. Amino acids in the nutrition of excised tomato roots. *Plant Physiol.* **12**: 793–802.

——. 1937c. Vitamin B_1 in the nutrition of excised tomato roots. *Plant Physiol.* **12**: 803–811.

——. 1938a. "Root-pressure"—an unappreciated force in sap movement. *Am. J. Bot.* **25**: 223–227.

——. 1938b. Accessory salts in the nutrition of excised tomato roots. *Plant Physiol.* **13**: 391–398.

——. 1939a. Potentially unlimited growth of excised plant callus in an artificial nutrient. *Am. J. Bot.* **26**: 59–64.

——. 1939b. Controlled differentiation in a plant tissue culture. *Bull. Torrey Bot. Club* **86**: 507–513.

——. 1939c. Glycine in the nutrition of excised tomato roots. *Plant Physiol.* **14**: 527–538.

——. 1940a. Does "C. P. grade" sucrose contain impurities significant for the nutrition of excised tomato roots? *Plant Physiol.* **15**: 349–354.

——. 1940b. Sucrose vs. dextrose as carbohydrate source for excised tomato roots. *Plant Physiol.* **15**: 355–358.

WHITE, P. R. 1942. "Vegetable Dynamicks" and plant tissue cultures. *Plant Physiol.* **17**: 153–164.

———. 1943a. *A handbook of plant tissue culture.* Lancaster, Pa.: Jaques Cattell.

———. 1943b. Nutrient deficiency studies and an improved inorganic nutrient for cultivation of excised tomato roots. *Growth* **7**: 53–65.

———. 1945. Respiratory behavior of bacteria-free crown-gall tissues. *Cancer Res.* **5**: 302–311.

———. 1946. Cultivation of animal tissues *in vitro* in nutrients of precisely known constitution. *Growth* **10**: 231–289.

———. 1949. Prolonged survival of excised animal tissues *in vitro* in nutrients of known constitution. *J. Cell. Comp. Physiol.* **24**: 311–316.

———. 1950. A plant physiologist looks at the cancer problem. *Sci. Mo.* **67**: 187–192.

———. 1953a. An efficient apparatus for the redistillation of water for biological purposes. *Proc. Soc. Exp. Biol. Med.* **82**: 671–673.

———. 1953b. A comparison of certain procedures for the maintenance of plant tissue cultures. *Am. J. Bot.* **40**: 517–524.

WHITE, P. R., and A. C. BRAUN. 1942. A cancerous neoplasm of plants. Autonomous bacteria-free crown-gall tissue. *Cancer Res.* **2**: 597–617.

WHITE, P. R., and E. LASFARGUES. 1949. Some effects of dilution on the nutritive value of dialyzed plasma and embryo juice. *Proc. Soc. Exp. Biol. Med.* **71**: 479–484.

WHITMAN, C. O. 1893. The inadequacy of the cell-theory of development. *J. Morph.* **8**: 639–658.

WILMER, E. N. 1933. Studies on the growth of tissues *in vitro*. II. An analysis of the growth of chick heart fibroblasts in a hanging drop of fluid medium. *J. Exp. Biol.*, **10**: 323–339.

WILSON, HILDEGARD, ELIZABETH B. JACKSON, and A. M. BRUES. 1942. The metabolism of tissue cultures. I, Preliminary studies on chick embryo. *J. Gen. Physiol.* **25**: 689–703.

WIRTH, J., and G. BARSKI. 1947. Cultures epithéliales pures sur membranes plastiques sans repiquages et sans plasma: prolifération rapide de cultures colorables comme des frottis. *Ann. Inst. Pasteur* **73**: 987–1002.

WOODWORTH, J. 1699. Some thoughts and experiments concerning vegetation. *Philos. Trans. Roy. Soc.*, London, **21**: 193–227.

INDEX OF NAMES

INDEX OF SUBJECTS

References to subjects are in regular type, plant and animal names in *italics*. Page references in italics refer to figures.

227